Your book, "Let It Flow", is an excellent attempt to educate the patient or potential patient about some of the newer concepts of healing and health maintenance particularly in regard to the natural and energetic aspects of health. The body was created to be a self-healing, self-perpetuating organism. Everything the body needs can be found within the organized expression of the life force as it manifests through the body's survival systems. What has been needed was the knowledge to unleash this healing force. This knowledge has been acquired from many disciplines both ancient and modern.

Your description of how these energies are applied to the body to bring about the optimum expression of health is clear and relevant in today's health crisis. As more and more people seek alternative therapies to the medical model, these therapies need to be known and understood by the public. I think that "Let It Flow" accomplishes this. It discusses the various alternative therapies that work and fulfills the public's need to know and understand at least something about them so that they can participate in their own recovery.

I recommend that all patients and prospective patients read this important book.

Dr. Carl A. Ferreri D.C. Ph.C. S.K.

Let It Flow

Hands-on techniques for healing the body, mind and spirit

Dr. Sheel Tangri BSc. D.C. S.K.

Canadian Cataloguing in Publication Data

Tangri, Sheel, 1965-
  Let it flow

  ISBN 1-55212-437-1

  1. Mind and body therapies. 2. Self-care, Health. I. Title.
RA776.5.T36 2000   615.8   C00-9109

To order this book online go to www.trafford.com/robots/00-0102.html
or www.trafford.com and use Trafford Catalogue #00-0102

For more information and to contact the author go to www.drsheeltangri.com

Let It Flow

Table of Contents

"I want to know God's thoughts,
the rest are details."

Albert Einstein

A MODEL FOR HOLISTIC HEALTH AND HEALTH CARE

INTRODUCTION

People often ask me, "What do you do in your treatments?" and I find that no matter what I say or how well I explain it, the individual cannot really comprehend the true nature of what I do through words alone. It is experiential as well as technical. The truth is, I have learned over half a dozen techniques that deal with the body's physical, emotional, chemical, and spiritual aspects and I employ all of them in my practice. Each person is like a book that must be read on all four levels if I am to really assist them. If one or more of these levels are not taken into consideration, only part of the problem will be corrected and the health imbalance may persist.

Unfortunately today there is a failure to acknowledge and treat all facets of the individual in concert. As a result many health conditions persist and are eventually labeled "chronic." This usually results in either a person being treated for years and years to no avail, or their symptoms being suppressed. In the latter case, doctor and patient rejoice in the apparent success of the treatment but as time passes, sometimes many years, the problem suddenly returns for no obvious reason and the original treatment becomes ineffective.

Why do the symptoms resurface? Because the root cause was not addressed the first time. The body has been pulled out of harmony with its environment and is asking us to pay attention, telling us there is more that needs to be addressed in order to allow true healing to take place.

This book is an attempt to give the reader a theoretical rather than a technical understanding of the different techniques that I incorporate in my healing practice. I will not explain how the various conditions are corrected, but rather why they are present and the effects they are having. The technical aspects are reserved for another forum, seminar or presentation.

In the past, people have been concerned with having a problem quickly corrected rather than understanding how it was caused. Today, however, people have begun educating themselves. They are seeking caregivers who will enlighten them about the workings of the body, mind and soul and help them co-create wellness in themselves. This is one reason why I never use the word "cure." A patient who asks a doctor or health practitioner to cure them is giving their power away, and abdicating their own responsibility. I believe the body has an innate intelligence that knows exactly how to stay in balance with itself and its environment. The power that made the body is the power that heals the body - we should listen to it and trust in its infinite intelligence to guide us. When we fail to listen to this intelligence, we move out of balance and block its flow. The way to return the body to balance and health is simply, to let it flow again. This is where the real cure lies.

My intent in writing this book is to explain how health conditions - many of which have been labeled chronic, inherited or untreatable - can in fact be treated and often corrected in very few sessions. It is important to note that the hands-on procedures I use to unblock energy are done without the aid of any drugs or other foreign substances. Taught to me by different teachers around the world, many of these techniques, though appearing to be new age or cutting-edge by today's standards, are actually deeply rooted in long revered systems, philosophies and doctrines of the past.

I am forever grateful to my teachers and masters, and in keeping with their original spirit, I am continuing to combine their knowledge and techniques with my own findings and inspirations. By applying the principles and practices outlined in this book, I envision a new global model for health care that incorporates many of these present day breakthroughs with time-honored techniques and knowledge of the past.

Health care is one of the most critical financial burdens of any country, but by using these methods I believe a more cost-effective health and wellness system can be implemented. It would eliminate unnecessary treatments and tests, and avoid the expenditure of time and money on therapies that may only become effective after other techniques have first been applied.

Some of the methods outlined here have a proven scientific basis while others do not as yet. This does not mean the latter should be disregarded or rejected. It simply means that the financial support or corporate will to look into many of these so-called "alternative" methods is not available yet. Meanwhile these methods should be given a fair chance and I appeal to any readers who are able to test, research, fund, promote and implement the methods covered in this book to contact me via:

www.drsheeltangri.com

CHAPTER 1

A WAY TO THE SOURCE

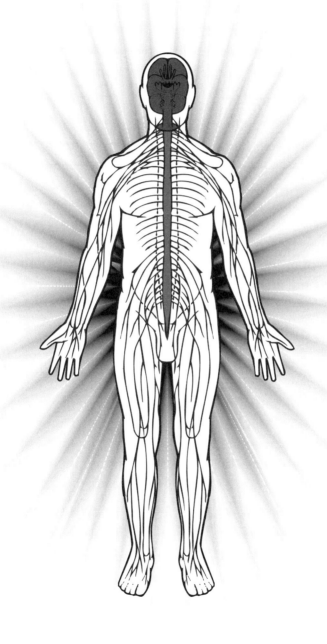

"The nervous system controls and coordinates all of the organs and structures, and relates the individual to their environment"
Grays Anatomy, 13th edition

When I was a very small boy I used to walk up and down my father's back. He had been injured by a severe blow to his spine many years before, and suffered from back pain and stiffness. When he came home from work in the evening he often used to lie down on the floor and ask my sister or me to massage his back. Being older and stronger, my sister used her hands, but I was much smaller so I would stand on him and work his back with my feet, as some masseurs do in Asia. As time passed and my sister went away to university, I took over the massage duties completely and by the age of about 11 or 12 my hands had developed a finely tuned sensitivity to the muscles of his neck and back. I could actually feel the tension spots where my father was hurting, and adjust my focus exactly.

This was the beginning of my journey into the healing arts and of my enduring fascination with techniques to ease physical, emotional and spiritual pain. Those early seeds were deeply sown and after taking a general science degree at the University of Manitoba I took a second degree at Palmer College of Chiropractic in Davenport, Iowa, the founding school of chiropractic. Since receiving my Doctorate in Chiropractic I have continued to expand my knowledge by learning many different techniques, and studying with many great teachers from here to India.

Unlike medical doctors who learn pathology and biochemistry in depth, chiropractic doctors learn an immense amount about neurology and technique. The practice of chiropractic, which began in about 1895, deals with the structure of the human body, particularly the spine, and its relationship to the **function** of the nervous system. It looks at what interferes with the link between frame and function, it looks at what impedes energy flow. My fundamental education as a chiropractor taught me the science, art, and philosophy of treating conditions without using drugs. It also showed me the body's inherent desire and ability to survive and maintain balance with its environment.

On a physical level, the nervous system acts like a complex computer that receives, assembles, correlates, stores and processes information in accordance with a program. It is a major receiver, regulator, and transmitter of life forces to and from the body and is responsible for almost every function within it. There are numerous pathways and circuits along which "electricity" travels as it directs the hundreds of functions (or programs) operating in the body at any one time: everything from the regulation of blood pressure and blood sugar levels to the processes of digestion, circulation and thought. It is absolutely staggering to think how much our bodies do for us every single day - let alone in a year, or a lifetime.

Like any highly functioning system that has thousands of moving parts, wear and tear is inevitable and as the old saying goes, an ounce of prevention is worth a pound of cure. Even the most highly sophisticated computer needs maintenance. Its circuits must be tested, adjusted and corrected by a skilled electrician who understands the blueprint or "schematic" of how the computer was constructed. Such an expert can run swiftly through these circuits, testing all the points in sequence, diagnosing trouble spots and repairing minor faults or "blown fuses" before they result in a systems crash. Not only does this ensure optimal system performance, but it is also cost effective.

Now, thanks to the recent discoveries of Applied Kinesiology and Specialized Kinesiology it is possible to do exactly the same thing on the human body, to run a diagnostic systems check of the nervous system. The body's circuits can be systematically tested and minor problems in function can be corrected before they become major concerns or chronic conditions. The potential savings in medical costs, not to mention human suffering, are staggering.

The roots of this new technique stretch back to 1964 when Michigan chiropractor Dr. George Goodheart discovered, and then began researching and developing the principles and practices of Applied Kinesiology. An eclectic blend of biofeedback, Chinese acupressure, emotional stress release, neuro-lymphatic massage and energy manipulation, Applied Kinesiology is a powerful natural therapy that can benefit anyone.

It treats the body as a complex machine and deals specifically with the link between the nervous system and the body's functions. It is an ideal, non-invasive wellness tool and, perhaps most importantly, it does not involve frequent or numerous spinal corrections as found in many of the mainstream chiropractic offices. It relies instead upon gentle rubbing or pressure upon specific points. The less force used, the more dramatic the results in most cases.

Recent research, as well as many ancient and time proven health methodologies such as acupuncture, have revealed that each organ in the body has a specific neurological connection to a corresponding muscle, spinal segment, acupuncture meridian, and set of lymphatic glands. For example, the liver is an organ that is largely responsible for filtering blood and keeping it as clean as possible. It has a **neurological** connection to the pectoral muscles on the front of the chest that move the arms. The **spinal** area that transmits nerve impulses between the brain and liver is found in the mid-back or mid-thoracic region. There are specific channels of energy flow - called **meridians** in acupuncture - and one of these affects liver function. There are glands in the body called **lymphatic glands** that act as a drainage system for the body, as well as carrying proteins, hormones and fats to all cells. Each organ has an energy connection to a specific lymphatic gland as well, hence the term **neuro-lymphatic reflex**.

All of the above mentioned act very much like circuit breakers or switches that can get turned off when the system is overloaded. When making corrections to the body's systems through Applied Kinesiology, all of these pathways must be checked to see if they are functioning properly. If not, they can be corrected so that energy has a clear conduit along which to transmit messages.

How is it possible to determine which "circuits" are functioning correctly? This is achieved through a process called "manual muscle testing" or "muscle response testing". It involves a doctor or therapist asking a patient to hold a particular muscle, their arm for instance, in a certain position. The therapist then applies a slight force to that muscle and the patient is asked to resist it.

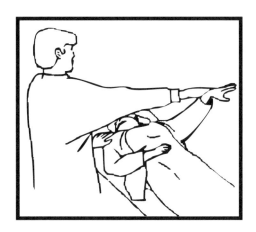

This simple exercise reveals not only the integrity of the arm muscle but also the integrity of the nervous system that feeds it. If the patient can offer solid resistance, then that "circuit" is clear and that nerve-to-muscle pathway can then be used as an indicator to reflect the integrity of other body pathways.

The therapist can now systematically touch certain key points on the patient's body (or have patients touch their own) while the arm muscle resistance test is repeated. If the patient's muscle offers resistance, the energy is flowing correctly. If the points being tested are not functioning appropriately a curious thing is observed by both therapist and patient: No matter how hard the patient tries to resist, he or she cannot make the muscle perform as desired.

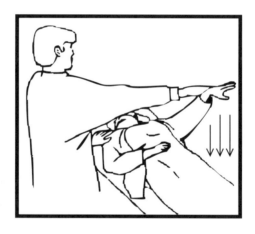

This phenomenon often arouses skepticism in even the most open-minded but a simple demonstration is all it takes for a new client to become convinced of its authenticity. The technique works primarily on the human electrical field, so it really has to be experienced to be believed. What is even more intriguing, and gratifying, is that once the appropriate correction is done, the points can be retested and the muscle will show full strength. (The term muscle testing is actually somewhat misleading for a therapist is not testing the strength of the muscle, but rather the integrity of the circuit in question. The muscle is merely the indicator, very much like the tiny light bulb that goes on or off in an electrician's circuit tester.)

Since the discovery of Applied Kinesiology (AK) and muscle testing in the mid-1960s, kinesiologists around the world have been correlating their findings and noticing intriguing patterns for scores of different health conditions. Patients suffering everything from stiff necks to poor bladder function and learning disabilities can now have their "circuits" checked and corrected - and be amazed to find overnight relief from long-standing chronic illnesses. Even more significantly, it is possible for kinesiologists to check the circuits of children and correct problems before they have developed into symptoms.

Now that is real preventative health care.

Let it Flow

CHAPTER 2

MY APPROACH TO HEALTH AND WELLNESS USING THE TRIAD OF HEALTH

"Get the big idea, and all else follows."

B.J. Palmer, pioneer of chiropractic

At its most fundamental and primitive level, life depends upon surviving in the jungle. Those individuals who adapt to their environment will survive and thrive through natural selection. Ideally, their bodies will function at optimal levels, in balance with the environment and in an efficient state of homeostasis. Hopefully, they will also be conforming to the definition of health as described in Webster's dictionary, which is "an optimum state of physical, mental and social well being, and not merely the absence of disease or infirmity." If a person is not functioning or feeling well physically, however, they will not be in a state of physiological balance and this will have a negative effect on their clarity of thought and action. Their relationships with family, society and their environment will also start to suffer - in other words, they will not to be able to survive as well in the jungle.

When you examine the "jungle" from a modern or even an historical perspective there are only three main categories of stressors that affect us. They are the structural, the chemical and the emotional - which is why I follow a model called the Triad of Health. Simply put, the Triad of Health looks at these three broad areas of external influence which feed into our human computers and affect the way we think, feel and act. When in balance these forces form an equilateral triangle as seen here.

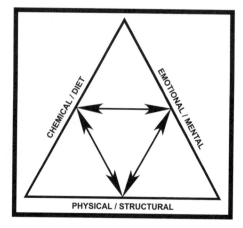

Whenever a person experiences poor health, however, one of these variables is out of kilter. In the case of a severe health challenge or chronic problem, two or even all three may be skewed and contributing to the situation of ill health. A simple example would be the case of an athlete who pulls a muscle in his mid-back which results in a spasm that pulls the fifth thoracic (a mid-back vertebra) out of alignment. The nerve passing through this location is partly responsible for supplying energy or power to the liver. Irritation and injury in this region may compromise liver function, which includes cleansing the blood of toxins or impurities. In other words, this injury to the back may now result in the patient not being able to tolerate certain foods - like caffeine or shellfish - and gradually becoming more toxic as he cannot eliminate properly.

This example can also work the other way around because nerve pathways are two-way streets. A person who is drinking too much coffee (a toxin of the bloodstream) or eating too much shellfish may place excess stress on their liver which then causes increased or hyperactivity to the pathway from the liver to the spinal cord to the brain. This can result in weakness at the level of the fifth thoracic vertebra, which then leads to a chronic backache. I've seen many patients who have fruitlessly visited a plethora of health professionals to cure their sore back, when the solution was as simple as cutting back on coffee or adjusting their diet. I have also seen many patients whose food sensitivities disappeared when their back problem was corrected.

When correcting the cause of any imbalance all three factors - structural, chemical and emotional - must be taken into account so that therapeutic efforts can be targeted at the underlying cause of a problem. This is the consummate beauty of Applied and Specialized Kinesiology. Its techniques enable me to evaluate the triad's state of balance, trace the problem back to its precise root, and assist the body to repair itself. It is vital to understand that a physical symptom may have an emotional or chemical cause, or vice versa. The bottom line is: If the primary factor remains untreated, the condition will persist or even worsen, requiring repeat treatments which are costly and time-consuming to the patient, not to mention ineffective in the long run.

ASPECTS OF THE TRIAD OF HEALTH

Physical/Structural

The physical side of the triangle has to do with bumps and blows, starting with the natural forces of childbirth and continuing through the normal accidents, falls and sports injuries that we all experience in everyday life. These can disorganize the physical alignment and functioning of the body, represented by the structural side of the triangle. When a person receives a structural affront - perhaps they have slipped and fallen on an icy sidewalk or sustained whiplash in a car accident - the "physical" side of the triangle can be thrown out of balance. This can then create increased emotional strain and dietary sensitivity, offsetting those two sides of the triangle.

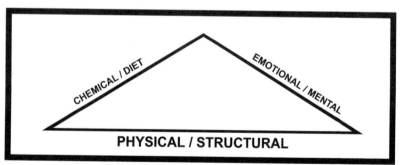

Since the cause of the imbalance was physical, the treatment should involve physical corrections to the nerves, muscles, bones, joints and organs through such strategies as massage therapy, chiropractic, acupuncture, cranio-sacral therapies etc.

Mental/Emotional

Any old emotional stress which has remained unresolved - divorce, abuse, childhood trauma, etc. - can affect the "emotional" side of the triangle. Such traumas, even when individuals think they have been dealt with, may remain energetically stored in the body and may pull the triangle, not to mention the body, out of alignment and harmony.

Emotional upheaval can have profound physical effects on the body. Just think of a person with low self esteem, how slouched their posture can become, or look at a chronic worrier who develops a rash whenever under pressure. The consequences can also be seen on the chemical side of the triangle, in reduced energy levels or diminished ability to metabolize nutrients. For instance, a chronic worrier may lose their appetite or experience irregularity.

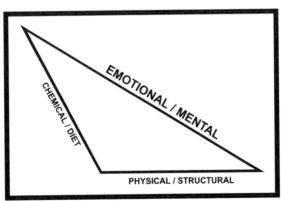

Emotional stress can sap a person's energy to the point where they get stuck in old thought patterns despite their desire to change and move on. Until recently, psychology, psychiatry and counseling were the standard treatments for emotional problems. While these therapies are very effective, often the memories or traumas that have become trapped in the subconscious are hard to access by the conscious mind (i.e. talk therapies) and take many sessions or years to dissolve and resolve. New techniques have been developed, however, that use muscle response testing to very efficiently and quickly access and release the emotional trauma from where it has been stored in the body.

Chemical

On the chemical side of the equation, an overuse of toxic substances such as nicotine, caffeine, alcohol, drugs and medicines, or a lack of essential nutrients, vitamins and minerals can impact the physical and emotional sides of the triangle. Poor nutrition can fatigue the organs and systems that fuel and sustain the physical body. With diminished energy it is clear that an individual feels more emotionally sensitive, less mentally alert, less able to deal with life's everyday stresses

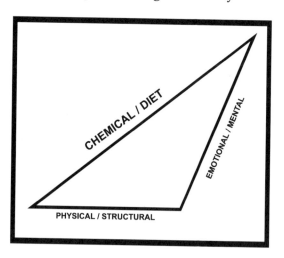

Chemical imbalances are corrected by eliminating harmful foods, modifying the diet by fasting and cleansing the system, or by introducing vitamins, minerals or herbs. Dietary changes are largely the responsibility of each individual. Each person is in control of what they eat, drink and smoke. My responsibility is to use kinesiology methods to identify which particular stressors or noxious substances need to be eliminated, and which positives should be added.

There are a multitude of specialized techniques that have developed from Applied Kinesiology, thus giving birth to the term Specialized Kinesiology. Some deal with detection and correction of emotional "faults," while others deal with physical or chemical concerns. I continue to take advanced training in techniques that deal with all three sides of the Triad of Health so that I can improve my abilities and effectiveness. This approach avoids the trap of needing to give multiple treatments for the same problem over and over. When the correct treatment is determined and applied the first or second time, the problem should not return, and in my years of experience, it does not return, unless of course there is new trauma.

A clear understanding of these concepts is essential before moving on to the next chapters, which describe the principles behind the techniques that I use, and how they are integrated.

Let it Flow

CHAPTER 3

THE PHYSICAL BODY

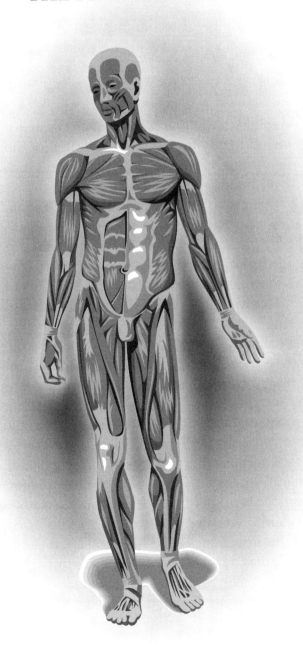

"You are what you is"

Frank Zappa

A wide range of techniques can be used to treat the physical body. Some address bone and joint function, some embrace the muscles and soft tissues, and some deal with treating or cleansing the various organs of the body.

As stated in Chapter 1, the nervous system controls the body, which in turn commands the muscles to either switch on or off. Therefore it stands to reason that when a muscle spasms it has been ordered to do so by the nervous system for a specific and intelligent reason. The body is usually trying to warn us that there is a structural misalignment somewhere that could result in major damage if the body is pushed too far, while playing sports for instance, or performing hard physical labor. Until the misalignment is fixed, the nervous system remains armed and the muscle stays in spasm.

The nervous system warns us that something needs to be taken care of while at the same time it is protecting the body from harm until the repair is made. Here is an example of how it works: A jogger develops a misalignment in his lower spine. There is no pain there so the jogger doesn't immediately realize he has a problem. Yet, when he goes for a run, the misalignment causes him to place more force on one side of his body than the other. This could result in major structural damage to the hip, knee or ankle on that side of his body, so his body goes into warning mode. The irritated structures and nerves in his lower back send his brain a red alert warning of potential damage and his brain responds by causing a muscle to tighten or spasm in the lower back and hip. This prevents the jogger from going beyond the threshold where he might seriously injure himself and have devastating results. To use the analogy of an electrical system: rather than overload the appliance and burn it out, a house is wired so that a fuse will be blown or the breaker thrown. This jogger has, in effect, blown a fuse as a means of protecting his body. This is why taking muscle relaxants in many instances are contrary to the body's wisdom and reasoning.

A muscle that continues to spasm can cause serious problems that go beyond the original injury or strain. It can change the alignment of bones to which it is attached, and create increased friction and degeneration of joint surfaces, which is why these warnings should be taken to heart and their causes corrected as soon as possible. Do not rely on the symptom of pain to be the indicator if you have a health problem or not.

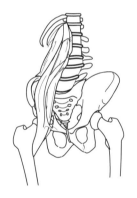 

When treating an injury such as this, a therapist can address the muscular component or the bone and joint component. If the problem is rectified and does not keep returning, it has probably been corrected. What I started to observe in my early years of practice, however, was that many people would keep returning with the same hip or lower back misalignment. They would try different exercises, modify their diet, change their shoes, be aware of not sitting with their legs crossed, or even stop performing the activities that they liked doing for fear that those might be the causative reasons for their recurring problem. I believed as I was taught at Chiropractic College, that the nervous system and the intelligence that runs through it has an innate desire to keep us well **if allowed to do so.** Therefore if a problem is persisting and requiring ongoing treatment, be it via mainstream or "alternative" therapies, the **cause** has not really been corrected. Before trying to modify any of the external variables in a patient's life, I want to be sure that the internal fuses that run their computer are working to their full potential. I believe that if the nervous system integrity is not examined and corrected as a primary modality, most health problems will remain uncorrected. I also believe that this is one of the main reasons why many conditions are improperly being treated or labeled as chronic. It also explains why our health system often supports the need for many treatments or medications over a protracted period of time.

The same principle holds true for conditions that involve the organs. Organ function either increases (becomes hyper) or decreases (becomes hypo) based on specific commands from the nervous system. A thyroid gland, for instance, does not decide all by itself to turn down its function and become hypothyroid. It is instructed to do so for a particular reason, by the master computer, and so the cure for the problem lies in discovering why the nervous system has responded this way. Sadly, many conditions have impressive sounding names, yet unimpressive amounts of time have been invested into figuring out why the body suddenly decides to jeopardize the function of some of its vital organs.

One can now begin to appreciate the value of Applied Kinesiology and other kinesiology techniques in providing diagnostic tools that can help us quickly identify and understand the function, and malfunction, of the body.

Neural Organization Technique (N.O.T.) is one of the most powerful techniques that I have been taught to date. It is the primary system that I use to assess and treat the physical body and I use it along with traditional chiropractic techniques and muscle therapies that I learned during my doctoral training. N.O.T was developed by Dr. Carl Ferreri, a chiropractor from Brooklyn, New York, who was among the first Chiropractic Kinesiologists to use muscle testing in the diagnosis, correction, and continuing reevaluation of health conditions. Also educated in acupuncture, cranio-sacral therapy and other healing arts, Dr. Ferreri is well equipped with knowledge of the body's circuitry and continues to work in this field.

I first met Dr. Ferreri in my second year at Chiropractic College. At that time, in 1988, his theories were well beyond what mainstream chiropractic professors were teaching. I went to his talk anyway and was fascinated not only by his theories but also by his approach. I myself do not advocate too many techniques or therapies to my patients unless I myself have experienced them. I received a treatment by Dr. Ferreri during that weekend seminar and I have to admit that it made a very significant change to my body. Even more impressive was that the condition never returned to this date. Many other doctors from many different disciplines have said that I either didn't have a problem or that it was a chronic degenerative condition. It was somewhat difficult for me to continue with my traditional chiropractic education for it felt limiting in its techniques. I do have a great respect for Chiropractic and will forever think of myself as one, however, I think that politics and health care can be a blinding combination. Unfortunately it is the patient and public who suffer when those holding the power and the dissemination of knowledge refuse to pursue the truth.

After graduating in 1990, I worked to develop my skills as a chiropractor for a couple of years, in Victoria B.C., but once my practice was established I found a significant number of patients were not getting long-lasting results. So in 1992, I remembered the amazing lecture I had heard and started studying Dr. Ferreri's work. Over the next three or four years I went to about 15 hand-on seminars in New York, Los Angeles, and San Francisco to study with him. I became a certified practitioner in 1994 and am now a certified instructor, one of only a handful in Canada.

The basic tenet of chiropractic philosophy is that all health problems involve some level of interference or disorganization of the nervous system. Therefore one of the most logical and **primary** treatments is to reorganize the nervous system and remove any energy interference. To use the electrical analogy again: If an appliance is not working we don't immediately take it in for replacement, first we check the plug and power source to see if the energy is flowing.

Back in the 1960s, Dr. Ferreri was working as a traditional chiropractor, treating many typical cases of headaches, neck, jaw, and back pain. Then he started using Applied Kinesiology as well. He had astonishing success with conditions that seemed to involve an even deeper disorganization of the nervous system - such as allergies, learning disabilities (ADD/ADHD), epilepsy, cerebral palsy, hormonal and fertility problems. Yet he was curious why some people responded immediately and permanently to treatments, while others held the correction for only a brief period, sometimes just a matter of days or weeks. He believed that if a condition was fixed it should stay fixed and not need repeat treatments - unless, of course, there was new trauma - because at the primitive neurological level a condition that is not immediately resolved could lead to death.

While searching for answers among 25 years of clinical notes, Dr. Ferreri started to observe patterns unique to individual conditions. For example, he found that both adults and children with learning disabilities always showed a particular sequence of cranial bone misalignments (which are very easy to gently correct, with dramatic results). With bed-wetting and people who had trouble holding their urine, for instance, there was always a specific jaw misalignment, acupuncture meridian blockage, and diaphragm weakness.

Using muscle-testing procedures, Dr. Ferreri began correcting only those faults that were consistently present with particular conditions, and by doing so he found that the results were much more accurate and lasting. By applying his broad knowledge of several disciplines he found an order and pattern in the nervous system, a kind of electrical blueprint. This insight had been lacking within each individual discipline but he came upon it through distilling the best from each technique, always taking his cues from the body. If a condition returned or a corrected circuit was found "blown" again on a subsequent treatment, Dr. Ferreri deduced that the body was directing him toward the involvement of a more dominant circuit that must be corrected first.

Through muscle-testing and the deeply intuitive work of pioneers such as Dr. Ferreri we can now demonstrate the existence of linear and sequential "programs" that govern the primitive functions of the human body, just as logical and rational programs govern the complex workings of computers. In fact, there is such reproducibility and accuracy in these N.O.T. protocols that if the reflexes are stimulated in a reverse order (for demonstration purposes) the condition **will return!** Clearly, when the body is spoken to intelligently, and in language it can understand, the response is swift and dependable.

PRINCIPLES OF NEURAL ORGANIZATION TECHNIQUE

Dr. Ferreri named his breakthrough method Neural Organization Technique because it organizes the human nervous system intelligently and specifically, so that it can function in the way it was designed, at peak performance, not at a level that is just out of pain or "barely getting by". Best of all, the hands-on method is effective when treating either symptomatic or asymptomatic conditions.

There is very little guesswork in N.O.T. and the treatment involves very specific corrections done in a precise sequence, so there is a beginning and an end point. Unlike other treatments that may require years and years of corrections, this methodology calls for only one to three sessions over a period of a few days. There is a high rate of repeatability and reproducibility, not to mention a high rate of success with most conditions.

On a scientific level, N.O.T.'s guiding principle is that in order to understand basic physiological functions we must look at our primitive origins. We were after all, created to exist and survive in a hostile environment. Therefore the tools we need for survival - with the exception of raw materials such as food, air and water - must be found within the body itself. Our bodies are designed to be self-healing, self-regulating, self-perpetuating mechanisms designed to repair and replace their own tissues. These mechanisms are innate, integrated and fully automatic from the beginning of life, yet the modern world's physical stresses, emotional trauma, poor diet and sedentary lifestyle can upset these automatic, inborn functions.

N.O.T. is the key to unlocking and understanding why many of these self-contained mechanisms break down.

Human survival systems have been named for their primary roles: Feeding, Fight/Flight and Reproduction. These three functions are external survival systems which human beings employ for their existence. Internal survival is governed by the Limbic System, which combines the immune, repair, growth and cellular reproduction systems that are found within the body. Together these two systems create a cohesive life force. I will explain in detail:

FEEDING / DIGESTION

From the moment of birth human beings know how to take in food, digest it, and eliminate the byproducts. There are circuits that involve secretion of digestive acids and enzymes, as well as muscular circuits involved with swallowing, moving food along the digestive pathway, and eliminating it. All this is automatic and innate.

Disorganization in these systems can lead to symptoms of hypo or hyperacidity, inability to breakdown and absorb food and nutrients, constipation or diarrhea, gas and bloating. Colic is one of the most common diagnoses given to infants when digestive irritability is evident, but this is one of the earliest signs of neural disorganization according to the N.O.T. philosophy.

THE FIGHT / FLIGHT OR DEFENCE RESPONSE

This response involves the control of structural balance and tension of musculature, ligaments and bone - the physical elements that protect the body from potential threats. The central nervous system comprises the brain and spinal cord. Nature has

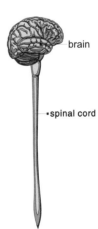

brain

•spinal cord

encased this "master computer" in a tough protective three layered membrane collectively referred to as the meninges. Like a sealed balloon, it is filled with cerebrospinal fluid, a liquid that acts not only as a shock absorber to cushion the brain and spinal cord when we move, but also to provide nutrients to the nervous system, resulting in electrolytic energy. To protect the central nervous system, nature has encased the soft nerves with a hard bony skull, spine and tailbone.

The cranium or skull is composed of 29 bones that move or articulate with one another during breathing. The spine is composed of 24 bones stacked one on top of the other to protect the delicate spinal cord which is like a big cable carrying all the information from the brain to the body, and back again. At the base of the spine is the sacrum, composed of five bones fused together.

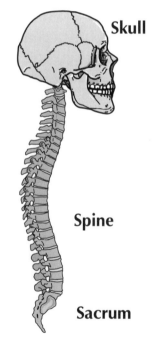

The meninges are attached to the inside of the cranium and the inside of the top three vertebrae in the neck. From there the meninges are basically free floating all the way down the spine until it attaches to the sacrum and coccyx (commonly referred to as the tailbone) at the bottom of the spine.

Skull

Spine

Sacrum

When an animal is in its normal resting state, the action of breathing causes movement of the cranial bones, the top three vertebrae, the sacrum and the coccyx. The meninges, which are attached to the previously mentioned structures, is subsequently pulled or tugged along as the bones move. This squeezing action causes the cerebrospinal fluid to circulate or pump around inside the meninges. This pump is called the cranio-sacral respiratory pump and is nature's way of keeping the fluids moving around and nourishing the central nervous system.

When an animal prepares for battle it goes into a defence or armed mode. It cannot let the brain and spinal cord rock around inside the skull and spine during a fight, since this could damage or bruise the soft delicate nerves. As a means of locking down the system the animal automatically clenches its jaw and throws its tail in the air.

When the jaw is clenched, all the cranial bones are clamped together, which stops them from moving. At the same time, inside the skull, the meninges tighten and anchor the brain so that it cannot jostle around and sustain an injury. At the other end of the spine, the tension on the tailbone causes the meninges to pull the spinal cord taut inside of the spine, thereby limiting movement and damage to those structures. This is nature's way of defending the most important structures in the body and securing the fortress against attack.

When the battle is over or a predator has been evaded, an animal in the wild settles down very quickly. Its spinal reflexes, tension, breathing and metabolism return to normal. Panting, gasping, yelling, roaring, crying and running are, incidentally, some of the primary ways that animals, including humans, reset their nervous systems and remove themselves from defence. This is why parents should allow their children to cry for a few minutes after they fall or injure themselves, or run around and yell to burn off excess adrenaline. Interestingly, I believe that this is why breathing exercises in health regimes such as yoga's pranayama are so helpful: deep breathing helps pump the cerebrospinal fluid and reset the structures of the spine and cranium, subsequently restoring optimum energy flow.

For humans, these fight/flight defence situations occur when coming out of the birth canal, falling and playing as children, taking part in sports as adults, or when we are involved in car accidents, etc. But people today also move into defence mode at other times: by drinking too much coffee or alcohol, working long hours at stressful jobs or just not exercising and breathing properly. The crucial point is, more and more frequently these natural reset switches are not being activated and people are getting stuck in defensive postures and states.

In my practice I am seeing more and more patients with disorganized defence systems that involve all forms of head, jaw, neck, back, hip, leg, and arm pains. They have difficulty holding their head up, they have severe muscle tensions, spasms and cramps - all due to their bodies being locked in semi-permanent or permanent defence mode.

REPRODUCTION / ENDOCRINE

In order for a species to survive, it has to reproduce. Not only does the reproductive system involve circuits that regulate sexual drive and activity, but it also involves other hormonally controlled functions. The glands in the body that produce and secrete hormones are known as the endocrine glands. They send out specific chemicals that control and regulate the level of sugar in the bloodstream, how food is metabolized, blood pressure, how quickly or slowly one will grow, and even how much an individual will sweat and produce heat.

Disorganization in this system may take the form of imbalances in blood pressure (dizziness when standing up too quickly or exhaustion after minor exertion), or with the blood sugar (hypo or hyperglycemia and eventually diabetes). Thyroid and adrenal dysfunction can be seen in rapid weight gain or loss, hot or cold hands and feet, or mood swings and emotional instabilities.

Many women complain about cramps or achy periods, irregular periods, heavy or light flow, pain during intercourse, lack of sexual desire, and difficulty becoming pregnant or giving birth. These all indicate that something is disorganized in the hormonal system function. The body is simply not producing the correct amount of hormones. Until now, the mainstream solution has been to chemically introduce hormones rather than to investigate why the body would fail to produce these vital chemicals. I recently treated a woman who was complaining of very low sexual desire. After neural reorganization she called to say she was feeling much better and her husband wanted me to know that the treatment was worth every penny.

Men are usually the last to admit they suffer from any sexual dysfunction, yet it is interesting to note the stampede of interest when a drug like Viagra appears on the market.

THE LIMBIC SYSTEM

The limbic system is an internal system that combines the immune, repair, growth and cellular reproduction systems. The immune system involves cells that combat foreign matter such as dust, pollen, viruses and pollutants. The repair system restores damaged tissues while the growth and reproductive systems maintain and replace aged or worn tissues.

Weaknesses in the limbic system can result in allergies, sensitivities, or even chronic and degenerative conditions that cannot be corrected or "cured" by medical science. Cancer is a perfect example of a system that has become wildly disorganized and has lost its ability to discriminate between normal and abnormal cells. All mayhem can result in a body where cells start to divide and multiply out of control. Science has shown that we all have cells in our body that are "cancerous," but under normal conditions other cells monitor and destroy them as soon they misbehave. They are then washed out of the body, leaving only the good cells behind.

When the limbic system is specifically turned back on, using N.O.T. protocols, the body of a formerly "disorganized" individual can "wake up" and start to remove these abnormal tissues in a matter of days or weeks.

Allergies point to another kind of disorganization, where the body has lost its ability to recognize and accept a normal substance in the environment. For example, when one is first exposed to bread, the body produces cells that acknowledge the bread molecule as a usable substance. It digests the bread, uses its energy and makes a "recognition file" which is stored in the brain. The next time bread hits the tongue, the body goes straight to the brain and checks its filing cabinet to see if it recognizes the substance. If it does, the body accepts the bread as "friendly" and begins the normal process of digestion.

In a disorganized nervous system, however, it is as if the files have been jumbled or cannot even be stored. The brain now believes that the substance is unknown or life threatening since it has no recollection of prior exposure. For survival reasons it rejects the substance by sneezing, watering eyes, coughing, vomiting, diarrhea, or reactions through the skin such as itching and rashes. It is very unfortunate that so much attention has been given to relieving symptoms - through taking medicines that stop coughing, dry up sinuses, or block diarrhea, for instance - when those are the very health-giving strategies that the body employs to try and heal itself. This is also a perfect example of how we sometimes work against the body and fail to honor its wisdom because we are too lazy or inept to see past the obvious symptoms.

Instead of avoiding foods or uncomfortable symptoms, we should be listening to what the body is telling us, and reprogramming it to coexist with the environment as nature intended.

THE PRINCIPLE OF N.O.T

In an organized nervous system the body's defence, digestive, and reproductive circuits are in balance.

Fight/Flight ------------ Digestion ------------ Reproduction

The body is ready to go into any one program at any time, depending on what is most needed at that moment. When the body is low on energy, for example, it increases power to the feeding systems and turns down energy to the fight/flight and reproductive systems.

When the digestive process has been satisfied - the stomach is full and/or elimination has been completed - the feeding circuits slow down and the energy to the fight/flight and reproductive systems is restored to their former levels. All day long we move in and out of these three states, depending upon what the "jungle of life" demands at that moment - at least, this is what happens in a normal, healthy organized state of being. In a disorganized state, however, the systems are out of balance and a person is stuck in one or other of these modes, usually defence. Now the human animal cannot survive efficiently in the "jungle" of life, and the groundwork for ill health has been laid.

Through trial and error, Dr. Ferreri discovered that the fight/flight system was usually the dominant trigger for neural disorganization. This means that at some point in life, possibly after a fall or trauma, an individual moved into the defence mode. The force or severity of neural disorganization was too great for the body to reorganize itself afterwards so the nervous system remained locked in defence, like a boxer, always braced for the next blow. This may explain why so many people complain of tension in the head, jaw, neck, and lower back.

My experience in treating more than 8,000 cases all around the world has been that these injuries usually occur in the first 5-10 years of life. This is the most staggering and important aspect to comprehend, since most conditions do not appear symptomatically until weeks or, more likely, decades later. At an early age, we all have significant falls or hit our heads. It's a fact of life.

Through muscle testing, a practitioner can test the integrity of the nervous system regardless of what the patient or the patient's parents may remember about the initial injury. Better yet, why not have the circuits checked immediately after a fall or accident? If not working properly, the function can be corrected immediately, without waiting for symptoms to appear. This is why it is so important to have children examined as soon as possible in life and why it is also important to base research on the causes of disease and discomfort, not the symptoms.

Research has shown that the majority of Cerebral Palsy, Attention Deficit and Down's Syndrome cases - conditions which all involve significant amounts of neural disorganization - also have weak immune systems. They present with symptoms such as frequent colds, skin rashes, food sensitivities, etc. If these studies had been done on people who first had their nervous systems reorganized, the research findings might have been completely different.

If not swiftly corrected the body stays locked in defence, the energy flowing to the digestive andreproductive systems are sacrificed, and eventually these systems will begin to show signs and symptoms of malfunction.

It is important to understand that when a body is locked in defence it will demand more energy and it will steal it from the digestive and reproductive circuits. On a primitive level, the human animal, like any other animal faced with an imminent threat, will obviously defend itself before taking time out to eat or procreate. This is why, when attempting to boost the digestive or reproductive systems, it is vital to disarm the defence system **first**. Working in another order would mean manipulating the body against its own intelligence, and would result in only a short-term correction.

THE "IN RELATION TO" FACTOR

Some people have headaches during the day whereas others complain of headaches at night. It was discovered that the nervous system must always be tested "in relationship to" the way it remembers the trauma. If the injury happened at night, the body will show weaknesses (neural disorganization) at night. At night or "in relation to the dark" was when the nervous system went into defence and subsequently turned down its energy flow to the digestive and reproductive circuits. If the kinesiologist is testing the circuits when the lights are on, the body will not show any weakness. However, when the lights are turned off the circuits will show the defect. The correction, therefore, must be made in the dark, either literally or figuratively. After years of clinical research it has been found that the body will respond to a verbal command by the practitioner of "it's dark", rather than actually having to turn off the lights.

I believe that the "in relation to" phenomenon is of major significance and is one of the reasons why many therapies fail to show high success rates. If we are to help the body regain its balance and optimum flow of energy we must talk to it in the way it thinks. Time and again I've seen car accident victims who showed complete organization of their nervous system when lying down on the treatment table, yet when the same tests were repeated in the sitting position all of their circuits showed weakness. This is because the person was in the sitting position at the time of impact/neural disorganization and the body is no longer completely safe in that position. The individual has no choice but to defend, until it is safely reset. His or her complaints of pain and inability to sit comfortably will persist until they are intelligently disarmed.

A good doctor or therapist must be a good detective and think like the body of a patient. The possibilities of how many "in relation to" factors exist are endless, but once the most common circuits are cleared (eyes open and closed, in the light and dark) the body can usually clear many of the other combinations on its own.

HOW AND WHY

Using the intact muscle strength indication system (the "muscle test"), N.O.T. procedures can determine the "blown fuses" in the basic survival systems. It can correct the fault in each system, so that the patient returns to neutral and is no longer stuck in low gear, or high gear, over-revving and wearing itself down. Defensive, digestive and reproductive systems return to their normal function, and the individual can operate in balance again, free of chronic problems.

People should never believe they have to "just live with it." Every condition has a cause and effect that is manifested through the nervous system so something can always be done. No condition is untreatable. We may not know enough yet, but we should continue to look for answers. That is what Neural Organization Technique is all about. Our motto is "IT IS N.O.T. IMPOSSIBLE."

For more information, contact:
Neural Organization Technique (N.O.T.) - Dr. Carl Ferreri
3850 Flatlands Ave. Brooklyn, N.Y. 11234
Phone: 718-253-9702   Website: www.notint.com

Let it Flow

CHAPTER 4

THE EMOTIONAL BODY

"You are what you think and feel."

Author unknown

After my first two years of studying and practicing N.O.T. on my patients, I found that occasionally I would perform a correction and the muscle test would still show a weakness. I would retry the correction but no matter what physical technique I employed, the circuit would not return to normal strength.

There is a saying that "when the pupil is ready, the teacher arrives" and so it was with me. My next teacher was Dr. Scott Walker, a chiropractor from Encinitas, California, and the founder of Neuro Emotional Technique (N.E.T.®). I began to study his techniques, incorporated them into my practice in 1993 and continued taking his seminars for the next two to three years.

Research has demonstrated that certain chemical messengers, called neuropeptides, are created in the brain and travel throughout the body whenever we experience an emotion. The power and influence of neuropeptides can be witnessed when a person is frightened by a snake, for example. The body may freeze, a wave of nausea may flood the stomach, or beads of sweat may start to trickle down the person's back. Even the sound of a snake's rattle or the picture of a snake can elicit a physical response in some subjects. Very often people dismiss such reactions as phobias and accept that nothing can be done to change it. They carry on with their lives, but are forever fretful and fearful of snakes whenever outdoors.

The exciting news is that this doesn't have to happen. It is now possible to change the body's response patterns and clear such negative reflexes quickly and easily. That is precisely what N.E.T.® is all about. By resetting the body's "emotional" computer we can unblock old sabotages, fears, and response patterns that chain us to the past. This is very important since the fear of suffering can often be worse than the suffering itself.

There are currently a number of different techniques that address the neuro-emotional component of human well being. They each have their own strategy for locating old response patterns and resetting the body to allow for new and more desirable ones. It is important to understand the basic theory.

When experiencing an emotion for the first time, a mother's kiss for instance, the body secretes neurochemicals via the nervous system and the result of this chemical reaction is that we "feel good". A positive stimulus-response pattern is created. In the future whenever that individual thinks about being kissed or sees an image of a woman kissing a child, the brain checks its "filing cabinet ", finds the previous favorable file in the nervous system, and the brain-body response is to "feel good", loved, accepted etc.

Conversely, when a father explodes at his three-year-old son for hitting a baby sister the result can be a defensive response, much like that discussed in the previous chapter. If the experience is highly emotional and physically stressful the body may not be able to reset or let go of the emotional charge related to the event. The youngster will then forge a stimulus-response reaction between mind and body that Dr. Walker has termed a Neuro-emotional complex or NEC. In this example the NEC created will relate to how the youngster will respond to anger or criticism from a male. From then on, whenever a male becomes angry or critical of them, they respond as previously programmed: defensively. Of course this can manifest itself in many different ways: as feeling combative, crushed, closed down, frightened, anxious or a wide variety of other emotions depending on the person's personality. This can also result in physical contractions such as tightened shoulders, clenched jaw and clenched fists. Even though an individual may not consciously understand it, every time a male directs anger at them - it may now be a teacher or employer - the brain sends a message to the body saying: "I don't like this, it doesn't feel good, it brings up old bad feelings, it is a threat to me." The body moves into defence. We must remember that the reason why these emotions are stored in the subconscious is so that the person can get through the trauma. It is a survival response. The event is painful or frightening or ugly, so the response is to hide the feeling deep inside and get on with life.

Such primitive stimulus-response patterns have likely existed in human beings throughout evolution, but modern science is now proving what the Chinese observed thousands of years ago: The "chi" or energy (the neurochemicals) of certain emotions connects with and is stored in certain organs, pathways or meridians of the body.

Anger, for example, is believed to be stored in the liver meridian, and the liver is an organ that has a multitude of physical functions in the human body. Largely responsible for filtering impurities out of the blood, it helps keep the immune system strong and, along with the pancreas, is a regulator of blood sugar levels. When the liver is weak it can cause blood sugar imbalances (hypoglycemia) which lead to ill health if a person doesn't eat over a short period of time. It can cause weakness in the immune system and result in recurrent colds and infections as well as a feeling of being generally run down. It can also refer pain to the mid-back and right shoulder, as these areas of the body specifically relate to the liver.

I treated a 40-year-old man who had experienced pain

in his right shoulder for some years and no amount of physical therapy gave him any relief. His body was indicating that the cause of the pain was emotionally related so I approached the case from the emotional standpoint, in order to properly correct the condition. It cleared within 10 minutes of the treatment and never returned.

I believe these programs are implanted as primitive fight/flight response mechanisms. The body thinks: "This is too much too deal with right now and I have other things that must be dealt with, so I will store this energy somewhere and get on with life." I also believe that such early responses are stored because parents fail to talk to their children or apologize after an emotional upset. By talking things through and learning to forgive and forget, we learn how to heal and let things go. Without early training in how to release anger and other stressful feelings, emotional upsets start piling up year after year until we are carrying a large cargo of negative baggage around.

Kinesiologists can use muscle testing to find out if the body is retaining emotional angst. We can access these subconscious thought patterns and beliefs, and reset the body's response so these patterns stop holding people back from living the lives they want to lead.

One way to access the "program" is to have a patient think of the pain and see if a muscle goes weak. If it does, they are then asked to touch two energy points located on the front of the forehead, which are related to the emotional circuitry. If a weak muscle becomes strong while the person is contacting the points and thinking of the pain (i.e. a change has occurred), it indicates a neuro-emotional component. If the muscle stays weak this indicates no emotional component at the time and the practitioner can continue looking for either a physical or a chemical cause. It eliminates guesswork for both doctor and patient, saves unnecessary treatments, time, and money - and employs the natural wisdom of the body.

Once an emotional component is identified, how does a healer unravel what the issue is and proceed to clear it? A verbal process, developed by N.E.T.®, is played between the doctor and the patient's subconscious using the muscle response testing. The body answers a verbal question with a "non-congruent" or "congruent" response that is provided via a muscle staying strong or going weak. This may cause some readers to raise their eyebrows but the process must be experienced in order to be truly understood.

An experienced practitioner develops the art of asking the right questions, narrowing down the field of possibilities, zeroing in on the problem and helping the patient interpret the answers. It is important to note that when this technique is used the patient is always fully conscious and assisting the practitioner, not in any kind of hypnotic state. The patient is not consciously answering any questions, however, he is letting his body speak for him through muscle response testing.

Here is the kind of dialogue that might take place when I am practicing this technique, using our previous example of the father who exploded with anger at his three-year-old son. The test child, now a grown man, is complaining about problems with his right shoulder. I believe it might have an emotional component so am working in that "program": Remember, I am talking out loud to his body and he is focusing on keeping the muscle strong rather than listening to the question and assuming the answer.

Dr: "Does this pain have to do with an event?"
    Test- muscle remains strong (means "non congruent" NC)
Dr: "Or a person?"
            Test-muscle goes weak (meaning "congruent" C)

Dr: "A female?"	Strong-"NC"
Dr: "A male?"	Weak -"C"
Dr: "A family member?"	Weak -"C"
Dr: "Your brother?"	Strong -"NC"
Dr: "Your father?"	Weak -"C"
Dr: "You and your father and anyone else?"	Strong -"NC"
Dr: "Only you and your father?"	Weak -"C"
Dr: "Does this have to do with you as and adult?"	
	Strong -"NC"
Dr: "Or as a child?"	Weak -"C"
Dr: "You between conception to birth?"	Strong -"NC"
Dr: "You between birth to five years of age?"	Weak -"C"
Dr: "You between birth to one year of age?"	Strong -"NC"
Dr: "You between one to two years of age?"	Strong -"NC"
Dr: "You between two to three years of age?"	Strong -"NC"
Dr: "You between three to four years of age?"	Weak -"C"

The technique resembles a game of 20 questions, or one that many of us played as children called Animal, Vegetable, Mineral where we deduced the answer by constantly narrowing the range of options. This process is played on a profound level, however, where the practitioner is literally communicating with the subconscious and does not assume anything. The reasoning mind is bypassed and the body is giving the answers as to what it holds a negative or positive charge to. At this point in our example we have located what Dr. Walker refers to as a "snapshot" of what the body has stored, and when. The man's body indicates the pain in his right shoulder has a neuro-emotional component tied to an incident that occurred when he was 3 to 4 years of age involving him and his father.

At this point the doctor does not know what the involved emotion might be. Chinese medicine, Chiropractic and Applied Kinesiology have found that there are reflex points specific to each organ of the body and they can indicate involvement with particular snapshots. So continuing with the same example, the liver point might show involvement when tested while the other organ points would not. Since we know that the liver meridian holds the emotions of anger and resentment, the doctor would pose the supposition as follows:

Dr: "Is the involved emotion resentment?"   Strong -"NC"
Dr: "Hatred?"   Strong -"NC"
Dr: "Anger?"   Weak -"C"
Dr: "Does this have to do with your anger at your father?"
                                                  Strong -"NC"
Dr: "Does this have to do with your father's anger at you?"
                                                  Weak - "C"

At this point the doctor may ask the patient if he recalls any situation where his father may have been angry with him at 3 to 4 years of age. Sometimes the patient will know of an event or have a vague idea. It is the responsibility of both the doctor and patient to assume nothing, and let the body reveal what it is holding onto. The body never lies and it remembers everything. If the patient says, "It's probably because I spilled my milk at the dinner table," then we must do a muscle test while they hold that thought. If the circuit tests strong then that event is not a stressor and is not the event we are looking for. If it weakens, however, we know we have hit the target and that this thought is still having a weakening effect on the body. Even if the patient has no recollection of an event, we can still clear the block because the body simply reveals its secrets by going weak (losing energy) whenever it is holding onto a negative charge.

We need to survive in the jungle and if something stresses us too abruptly, too harshly, or for too long, we stuff it away and move on to the next event. Over and over, these emotional upsets are stored in our subconscious minds and bodies until one day they overload the computer circuitry. That's when we have an unexplained emotional or physical breakdown.

As we grow out of childhood and start to gain a better understanding of this world, we all have certain idiosyncrasies that seem to hold us back from becoming who we truly want to be. Many people see psychiatrists or psychologists in an effort to recognize and change patterns. Such talk therapy is often important and empowering because it enables individuals, through trained professionals, to understand themselves and achieve solutions. The drawback is that while the emotions may be intellectually cleared, the stresses often remain **locked in the body** at a primitive level and the patient still has negative gut reactions related to their issues.

Unfortunately, some patients endure years of probing that fail to find the answers. So where does a person turn when they cannot remember the original event that caused their negative belief pattern or permanent defensive stance? Muscle response testing holds the key to unlocking these past responses because it provides immediate, accurate feedback.

Once identified there are many different ways of deleting or disconnecting a negative mind-body response. Some therapists do spinal adjustments or rub acupuncture points, some use breathing techniques or have patients do certain eye movements. My experience in defusing such responses is to urge patients to hold onto the particular **feeling** at the moment of correction. Even if they don't remember the event, they can hold the emotion in their mind while the experience is being "cleared." Those who are computer literate know that hitting the "delete" key is easy, the important thing is to have the correct information up on the screen.

When using this technique it is important to emphasize that we don't erase memories or brainwash people. We simply disarm or halt the <u>negative brain-to-body response</u> that was based on a previously learned event so that the person can respond to new events in a fresh, open way, not only mentally but physically too. They can live in the now, and physically start responding to events based on the present moment, not something in the past.

Once the correction is made, the doctor can test the area of pain again and see if there is still a weak muscle response. If there is, and the emotional points on the forehead confirm this, then another emotional event is present and must be dealt with. If the muscle test stays weak it indicates that there is not another emotional event but possibly a factor on the other two sides of the triad of health, namely the physical or chemical factors.

Many of the people who come to my office do not complain about any particular pain or symptom, but of just feeling "stuck" in life. They have difficulties in relationships, or obstacles to dieting, quitting smoking, etc., or they suffer from phobias. With these people we can access the program by having them make verbal statements and then seeing if their bodies stays strong during the statement.

For example, one could be asked to state: " I am okay with quitting smoking" but when I test a muscle while they say it, the muscle goes weak, indicating that they are not congruent with this statement. If a contact over the emotional centers makes it strong, I then begin the same procedure as described earlier. **Using the right words is important when accessing brain / body files.** "I'm okay with quitting smoking" is a different concept from, "It's good for me to quit smoking." The former could lead back to past issues dealing with a lack of self-worth/self respect, and the person's desire to care for themselves. The latter may deal with issues related to morality and public perception (i.e. smoking is bad). Since this is the faulty brain-to-body program - in other words "I don't value my body or myself" - any conscious attempt to value it through quitting smoking, exercising or dieting is going to fail because it contradicts what the subconscious brain-to-body response is programmed to do.

The body will always follow the mind's programming. This may help explain why some people actually follow the right diet or sign up for the best quit smoking program in the world, but the problem gets worse. We call this "emotional sabotage."

If the issue is properly and permanently cleared then the muscle response will stay strong, indicating they are now congruent with the thought not only in mind, but also in body. Dr. Walker calls this "emotional congruence." This does not necessarily mean a person will quit smoking immediately after a treatment, but an important psychological hurdle will have been cleared. The body is now able to support that new thought pattern.

The goal of this technique is to help people become emotionally congruent with every possible aspect of their existence, be it physically, materially, romantically or spiritually. I encourage everyone to seek the services of a qualified practitioner in this field because all of us have had emotional "upsets" in our lives and are probably holding onto some negative, damaging energy somewhere in our bodies. We must also let go of the feeling that if we have a problem we are weak or imperfect.

As the saying goes, "stuff happens." But people now have a choice. They don't have to carry that "stuff" around anymore because there are powerful techniques that can clear it away. I emphasize that people should not wait for a problem to surface, nor be paranoid that every little crisis will be creating stress and problems for them. Visit a practitioner for preventative care from time to time, and get on with living life the best you can.

For further information, please contact:

Neuro Emotional Technique
Dr. Scott Walker
500 2nd Street
Encinitas, California 92024
Phone: 619-944-1030   Website: www.netmindbody.com

CHAPTER 5

THE CHEMICAL BODY

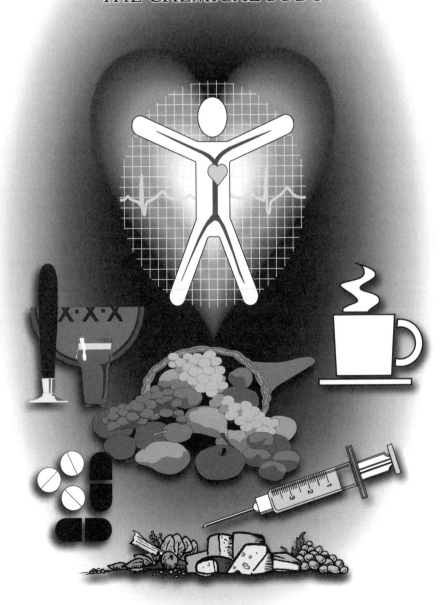

"You are what you eat."

Author unknown

There is a lot of confusion these days about diet and I sympathize with those who are bewildered by all the conflicting information and contradictory advertising hype. I believe the confusion stems from the fact that most diet research is done on people who have disorganized nervous system to begin with. This is why some diets work for some people and not for others, why some people find a nutritional regime effective in dealing with an ailment while others find no relief. Of course the results are contradictory when there is no consistency to begin with.

In this chapter I am not presenting another miracle diet. I am offering some basic guidelines that I have learned over the years, and patients have reported to be of great benefit, especially after a person's nervous systems has been reorganized. Through my study of numerous books on Chinese medicine, the Ayurvedic approach of ancient India and of western style nutrition, I have concluded that we should listen to our bodies and find out what really works for us.

I recommend that people follow this holistic model of health care: First, reorganize the nervous system to free it of physical and emotional interference. Second comes cleansing and working toward improved elimination. Next, we should work toward improving the diet which includes an increased awareness of pH balance; and then our aim should be to calm the system, reduce the stress and maintain balance in everything we do.

Going back to the triad of health, it is obvious that the

nutritional or chemical side of our existence is, for the most part, under our own control. **We** decide what we want to eat, drink, inhale, inject, or rub on our bodies. It is of the utmost importance, therefore, that we educate ourselves and take responsibility for the choices we make. For every raw material or stimulus the body is subjected to, for every piece of junk food we consume or vaccination that we receive, there is a physical response and probably an emotional response. We may not be able to control absolutely everything we ingest or breathe, since things like air pollution and genetically tampered foods may be beyond our control at this time. But it is important to make the best choices we can, while becoming advocates for better quality water, air and food supplies in our areas.

CLEANSE THE BODY THROUGH REGULAR FASTING

I find it amazing that we all recognize the need to change the oil in our cars, but few people give their own digestive tracts a thorough, regular cleansing. When was the last time you stopped eating for 24 hours? Perhaps when you had a flu virus or a bad cold. When that happened the wisdom of the body told you that it was clogged up and in need of some attention and rest. This is the basic concept behind fasting.

Even a short fast of 24 hours will allow the digestive system to take a break. The idea is not to strain the body to lose weight, but rather to allow it to rest and catch up periodically so that it does not become clogged to the point of non-function. If you agree that an ounce of prevention every day is worth a pound of cure, you can counteract many of the negative effects of modern diet and lifestyle. Every night, when we sleep and don't eat for 10 or more hours, we are doing a mini fast. Before you break your fast ("breakfast") and eat in the morning, it is helpful to clean out your pipes with the juice of half a fresh lemon in a glass of warm water. This is a very gentle way to wash away toxins that have become lodged in the digestive tract. It may sound like a small lifestyle change, but it can be a major step in the right direction.

The concept of fasting has been around for centuries and is a major tenet of many world religions. Some people fast for one day every week, three days every month, or 10 days twice a year as part of their ongoing health regime. Fasting can also be employed as a strategy by people facing life-threatening disease and I have known people to fast for 30, 60 or 90 days, consuming just water and juices during that time. Always check with a health professional (naturopath, colon therapist etc.) before embarking on a long fast, as these should be done in controlled and supervised situations. There are many health centers around the world that specialize in such treatments and many excellent books on the subject.

I fasted for 10 days once, and it was a fascinating experience. After two days my body was tired but after the fourth day on just water and lemon juice I had boundless energy. I managed to work on patients very effectively all day, and during the nights I had vivid dreams during which I felt cleansed my mind as well. I lost some weight, although that was not my prime motivation, but more importantly I learned about the overwhelming psychological attachment we have to food. Everywhere I looked while on my fast, I noticed advertisements for french fries, pop, sweets, and junk food. When I came off the fast I was much more attentive to the foods that I put in my mouth: It was like a rebirth of my relationship with food. I also started shopping differently, around the edges of stores, where all the fresh produce is, instead of down the middle aisles where all the boxes and processed foods are stacked. I gradually gained some weight back, but some pounds never returned and I like to think they were the ones that were filled with toxins and fat.

During a fast, many people report having bowel movements that appear black like tar. Think of a pipe coated with slime and you will understand what the black sludge is like in people's bodies. Just as a drainpipe gets clogged and needs to be periodically cleansed, so does the bowel, or else the results can be malabsorbtion problems, obesity, irritable bowel syndrome, colitis and even ulcers. Clogged digestion can also lead to skin rashes, acne, eczema, psoriasis, lung conditions and bronchitis. This makes perfect sense when you think that if you block the exhaust pipe of a car, the fumes and toxins will come out through the body of the car.

It is extremely important that after a fast one "washes out the pipes" of the dislodged debris, or else this loosened sludge will just be reabsorbed into the system. That's why for a few days after coming off a fast it is wise to just eat light soups and juices. Many times people stop a fast too soon because they don't feel well and start to get headaches or low grade fevers. This is often a sign that the body is just beginning to dislodge the old toxic debris into the bloodstream and the fast is having its effect. Even though one may not feel so good at the time, it is the time to persist and stay on the fast.

STAY CLOSE TO NATURE, EAT LOCAL FOODS IN SEASON

Once cleansing has been accomplished it is important to start eating as well as you can. My healing practice has taught me that the majority of our diet should come from locally grown produce because if you eat foods that are grown close to home they can be eaten at their best, ripest and most recently picked. When we eat foods that are picked before they are ripe, that are sprayed with fungicides so they don't spoil, trucked hundreds or thousands of miles, and stored or refrigerated for days or weeks on end, we are obviously sacrificing freshness and goodness. Taking this philosophy a step further, there are many opportunities now to purchase foods from local organic farmers on a year-round, contract basis. This not only supports healthy eating in our homes, but a new life-enhancing movement in our communities.

Stop buying food every two weeks and try shopping every day or two for what is most fresh and appealing. This is common practice in countries like France and Italy where many gastronomes and food purists are so fussy that they eat only the cheeses, fruits, vegetables and herbs that are produced in their own regions. Many of the cheeses in Tuscany for instance are raw and unprocessed, which means they must be eaten within two or three days or else they will spoil. Grocery shopping every day may seem unrealistic for some, but we should strive towards this goal in principle, and many organic producers now deliver to the door. Besides, spending a few extra minutes to shop daily may mean fewer days spent in bed with influenza and colds.

Post war studies in Southern England turned up some curious findings related to this kind of back-to-nature philosophy. After the Second World War, scientists were eager to study the deleterious effects of rationing on weary Londoners who had also been subjected to the added stress of bombings and fear of attack. The scientists were staggered to find that the incidence of diseases such as high blood pressure, diabetes and heart disease had actually plummeted during the war. They discovered that rationing of items such as butter and sugar, coupled with the increased consumption of seasonal vegetables such as cabbage, turnips and parsnips had a marked effect on the general health and hardiness of the population. People who dug up their lawns to plant vegetables out of dire necessity found their health and longevity improved.

There are other compelling reasons to eat locally, and one of them relates to the natural cycles of life. At certain times of the year nature produces foods which aid in keeping us energized during that season. When the days are shorter the local crops include things like root vegetables as well as apples and pears, that can be naturally stored for many months in the cold weather to come. Fruits like grapes, which ripen in the fall, are ideal digestive cleansers for the winter to come. At the end of the summer it is healthy to do a little detoxification of the bowels with a short grape diet, and the same goes for the spring, when fresh berries help clean out the winter energy and prepare us for the longer days to come.

I'm not suggesting people switch cold turkey to this kind of lifestyle, but we can all strive to modify our diets gradually in this direction. Again, I urge people to observe how their bodies feel when eating fresh, seasonal, local foods- and then make their own decisions. Pay attention to what you eat, taste your food, and enjoy it. If you really don't enjoy something, if that coffee and sugar-loaded pastry at 10 in the morning is just an old habit, then stop it. Try to become conscious of taste again and analyze whether you are eating for pleasure or just because of subconscious routine. Eat to live, don't live to eat.

I encourage people to drink six to eight glasses of fresh pure water (not from the tap) daily, and to take a good multivitamin and a good multimineral. Like batteries, we are made up of chemicals and water. To keep the battery functioning at its best we must replenish our chemicals and water with the best quality we can find.

One of the worst health habits many people have is drinking coffee on an empty stomach, first thing in the morning. My clinical experience has shown me that coffee ranks up there with alcohol and nicotine as one of the major causes of health problems in our society. I'm not suggesting we rid ourselves completely (well, perhaps I am) but most of my patients notice a big improvement in health after eliminating or radically reducing their coffee intake. They report withdrawal symptoms such as headaches for two or three days (so do heroin junkies) but after several days they feel their energy picking up and say they have never felt better or more vital. As an aside, how many people say that they are broke yet manage to find $3 a day for a latte or cappuccino. That adds up to $1,000 a year, and there are plenty of people who drink far more than one a day. If a person really loves the taste of coffee they should look upon it as a treat to enjoy a few times a month, like a special dessert.

TRY COMBINING FOODS

One diet modification that is highly effective for most people is based on the concept of food combinations. Certain foods, when mixed together, have positive effects on the body because they aid digestion, while other combinations can slow digestion and thereby deprive the body of energy needed to perform daily functions. Two books that I highly recommend are Harvey Diamond's *Fit for Life* and Dr. Jonn Matsen's *Eating Alive*. The former offers an in-depth explanation of the concept of food combining, while the latter is excellent for lay people who want to understand the physiological process of digestion and how to cleanse the body.

Food combining theory is based on the principle that different foods require different lengths of time to digest, and therefore should not be consumed together if one is aiming toward optimal health and digestion. Protein takes the longest of all foods to digest, and a steak can take many hours. Fruits, on the other hand, digest very quickly, often in a matter of minutes. When fruits and steak are eaten together they create indigestion because meat requires an enzyme called pepsin to digest it properly, and most fruit acids destroy this enzyme. When consumed with meat, the fruit starts to ferment, causing gas and acid indigestion. There are many good books on the subject and they are worth reading.

BE AWARE OF YOUR PH BALANCE, STRIVE FOR AN ALKALINE DIET

Once the body has been cleansed through fasting, and a person has started eating fresh, locally grown foods in correct combinations, it is a good idea to become aware of a simple principle in body chemistry.

In chemistry there is a system of measurement called the pH scale. It ranges from 0 (acid) to 14 (basic or alkaline). The optimum pH of the blood is between 7.37 and 7.41. If a person's blood pH goes out of this very narrow range they can swiftly become ill and go into a coma. The kidneys, considered one of the most important organs in Chinese medicine, regulate and monitor the pH, keeping it in an optimum range at all times. It is a phenomenal process that carries on during every second of our lives, a balancing of yin and yang to ensure the "battery" has the correct charge.

The body operates more efficiently and seems to stay younger when the diet is more alkaline. This occurs when the diet is comprised primarily of fruits, nuts, whole grains, and vegetables. When the diet is more acidic, the aging and degenerative process is accelerated. An acidic environment in the body is promoted by the ingestion of animal products like meat, milk, eggs and cheese as well as caffeine, white sugars, white flour products, alcohol, pop, processed foods, canned foods and nicotine. Keeping the acid-base balance in the correct range is the theory behind many food combining diet regimes.

FIGHT OR FLIGHT RESPONSE

Most of the patients I see appear weak and drained. The truth is, they are weak and drained, partly because the typical Western diet encourages a pH range that is way out of balance on the acidic side, but also because of stressful lifestyles.

As explained in Chapter Three, the body produces the hormone adrenaline in fight or flight situations. It is called a burst hormone because a small amount produces a huge response in the body. In nature, adrenaline is released infrequently, to give animals the tremendous burst of speed needed to avoid a predator or to attack their prey.

I believe that many problems arise in our society because many people are physically and emotionally stuck in defence mode all the time. This means that their adrenal glands are releasing a constant flow of adrenaline (hyper adrenal) causing the body to produce excess heat, sweating, and energy. Under normal circumstances the body produces heat and metabolism via the thyroid gland, and energy via the insulin/blood sugar mechanism regulated by the pancreas. The body never wants to waste energy, so when extra heat and energy are produced by an over-active adrenal gland, the body turns down the thyroid (hypothyroid) and insulin (hypoglycemia) gauges to balance things out.

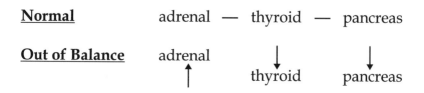

Normal   adrenal — thyroid — pancreas

Out of Balance   adrenal ↑   thyroid ↓   pancreas ↓

Remember that injuries causing an individual to stay locked in defense mode occur in the first five years of life. This will result in heightened adrenal activity. A child in a state of hyper-adrenalism will develop symptoms of hypoglycemia (low blood sugar) in their early years and this will lead to cravings for carbohydrates and sugars such as bread, pasta, candy, soda drinks - anything that will give them a temporary high to compensate for their decreased pancreas/insulin output. As they grow older, they switch to adult stimulants such as caffeine, pastries and chocolate. (Don't get me wrong. I love chocolate, but in moderate doses.)

Many parents of children who have been labeled "hyperactive" or as having Attention Deficit Disorder (ADD) may already say that I am describing their son or daughter. The solution for these children is not Ritalin (kiddie Prozac) and other mind numbing drugs, but the non-invasive approaches of N.O.T. that can intelligently and systematically help reorganize and clear the nervous systems of these hyper- or hypoactive conditions. N.O.T. can turn down the adrenals (by disarming the defense mode) and allow the body to restore energy and function back to the thyroid and insulin mechanisms. The sad reality is that most of us are in this state, since most of us have had falls or accidents which triggered the process of neural disorganization, and hence the move into defence mode.

If such disorganization is not corrected and the adrenal glands are forced to do more work than originally intended, they will eventually become fatigued or break down. I recently treated a patient who had for eight years been told she had Chronic Fatigue Syndrome and Fibromyalgia. She had been diagnosed with low thyroid and low blood sugar for which she had taken medications, and had also been on various diets that resulted in very little change, if not even adding more toxicity to her body. She could do nothing except sit. Standing up exhausted her. She stated that she had always been tired since her childhood years and was often sick with one cold or another.

When I saw her I did a neurological and emotional clearing as discussed in previous chapters and found that she had had a cranial injury and been stuck in defence since the age of about five. She had managed to get through life somehow but it was always a struggle. At 37 years of age her health began to nosedive and when I treated her at 49 years she was chronically tired, with continuous muscle aches, hypoglycemia and cravings for sweets and starchy foods. Her adrenals had been doing all the work, so instead of lasting 80 years they had collapsed with fatigue by the time she was half that age. After three sessions of N.O.T. over a period of two weeks she was back working in her garden and reported that she was functioning at a level she had not felt in more than 40 years.

When using N.O.T techniques this kind of testimonial is not uncommon, yet I never promote N.O.T. as a silver bullet. I see it as a very powerful technique, however, that should be given more attention globally and certainly employed as a first step in any healing modality.

It is a shame to pigeonhole patients into syndromes, diseases or conditions before first looking at neural disorganization. Far too often scientists spend precious time seeking viruses or bacteria as the causes of disease, instead of looking at the possibility of deeper individual causes and how they are affecting the whole. Many of the patients I have seen - especially those with birth or early childhood injuries - have spent the first 10 to 25 years of their lives stuck in hyperadrenalism (defence). When the adrenal gland eventually burns out and goes into a state of adrenal fatigue nothing seems to help these people maintain their daily energy levels, not even caffeine or sugar. They are chronically fatigued, achy all over, generally burnt out and depressed.

When working on a new patient, my approach is **always** to first employ the N.O.T. treatment protocols to eliminate any neuro-physical variables. I then check as many neuro-emotional variables as possible - and reset them. It is even possible to use muscle testing to find out if a person is reactive to a particular chemical substance, or benefiting from a particular food product. For example, one can place a grain of coffee on the tongue and then test a muscle. If the muscle weakens this indicates that caffeine is a stressor for that person, at that time.

This form of testing can be used not only for foods but also vitamins, drugs, herbs and homeopathic remedies that are being taken to rehabilitate the body. Sometimes there are surprises, as when a patient finds out that a particular vitamin or supplement they are taking is actually not doing them any good. It may be that the dosage is too high for them, or that the combination of products is not in balance. This is another area where muscle response testing has great value and can be used as a tool to seek feedback from the body.

Let it Flow

CHAPTER 6

EXERCISE, YOGA, MEDITATION AND PRAYER

"Make fun your exercise, and exercise your fun."

Dr. Sheel Tangri

When it comes to exercise, my basic philosophy is "use it or lose it." I encourage people to move, dance, play, laugh, study, practice yoga and go for long walks. Whatever they find entertaining and fun is what they should be doing - because they will enjoy it and, hopefully, do it regularly. Always aspire to make your life and others' lives as fun filled as possible. Do things that benefit your well being as well as that of others. The bottom line is: stay active, keep moving, try new things, turn off the television and GO.

No one can achieve their full potential if their nervous system is disorganized, and that goes for whether they are an athlete or an office worker, a teenager or an octogenarian. But for athletes especially, disorganization is one of the main reasons why so many sports injuries occur. The logical solution is to have the nervous system reorganized before beginning any new exercise program, no matter what the age or state of fitness.

Similarly, how can one effectively meditate and calm the mind if it is stuck in defence or weighted down by old emotional baggage? Having the nervous system cleared is one of the primary therapies in the journey back to wellness.

EXERCISE AND STRETCHING

Before beginning any new exercise program it is wise to check that the neurology is functioning properly. If for example the nerve supply is impeded or imbalanced on one side of the body, what is the point of doing extra push-ups or sit-ups? The muscle will not become stronger until the power is restored! Over-working a disorganized nervous system is not only ineffective, but it can possibly damage the body. I have worked on athletes and amateurs alike - everyone from golfers and weight trainers to long distance runners - and more than 80 per cent of them have reported dramatic increases in function and performance after N.O.T.

Stretching is an important aspect of exercise that is often overlooked. It is helpful before exercise because it prepares muscles, bones and ligaments for movement. **After** exercise it is equally important because it relaxes muscles and helps them to stay limber and elastic. Following a hard tennis game, for example, if you stop playing and immediately get in a car and drive home, your muscles will stay in a higher state of tension than normal. This prolonged contraction can cause stiffness within the next 12 hours, and possibly impede performance in the next game or lead to an injury.

MEDITATION

Meditation is a real asset in today's busy world. Many people believe it is something metaphysical and mystical, something beyond their capabilities. It is not. Life can be a meditation when you practice the art of being present, the ability to live in the now. By this I mean really seeing, feeling, hearing, tasting, and sensing what is going on inside and outside of yourself. There is also another form of meditation where you sit for a few minutes in the morning or evening, or both, to calm the mind, slow the respiration, and enhance inner peace. Take a few minutes in the morning, before you even open your eyes or get out of bed, to acknowledge what you have, what you want, what you feel, what is and what is not working in your life. You don't have to figure it out, just take the time to observe your thoughts. Don't judge your thoughts, and don't judge yourself. Just let it flow.

There are many books that explain different forms of meditation and various kinds of relaxation techniques, everything from putting one's attention on the breath, to using a mantra, to visualization. Personally, I practice Transcendental Meditation which is one of the most studied and researched techniques of its kind. It has been found to lower blood pressure, reduce heart attack risk and decrease stress. Through reading and trying different kinds of meditation, an individual can find the one that best suits them. It is then very beneficial to meditate regularly and incorporate the practice in a health regime, just like exercise.

YOGA

Yoga is another element in a healthy lifestyle, and an effective way to help keep the body and mind supple. Based on techniques that trace their roots back 5,000 years to ancient India, yoga combines physical movements and poses with meditation and controlled breathing. The fusion of these three leads to a closer connection between mind and body, and increased relaxation and awareness. Needless to say, it also increases strength, balance, energy, flexibility and boosts the immune system. A few minutes of yoga, performed morning and/or evening, can have a powerful impact on physical health and state of mind.

DAILY INVOCATIONS

Over the years I have come to appreciate the incredible power that the mind has over the body - and taking it one step further, the influence that the spirit has on the mind and body. Years ago I began encouraging patients to enliven their spiritual awareness, enabling them to create and make changes possible in their lives. Once cleared of the old energies and limiting thought patterns, through the various means discussed previously, the human being is a vessel ready to receive what is truly their birthright.

When I was about five years old I had a favorite puzzle, a little board with tiny squares that slid around. In the middle was a picture of two hands in prayer while around the edges were pieces that could be manipulated, and when correctly organized, spelled out the message: "Ask and it shall be given you." Doing this puzzle over and over again impressed my higher mind with this fundamental truth and I am extremely grateful for this profound early lesson. I have passed it along to many others.

Anything that we desire in life - whether it is better health, relationships or jobs - is within our grasp if we first ask our higher selves for it. Unfortunately, most of us don't ask, so doors remain closed to us, or if they are open we may be afraid or unaware of which ones to walk through. I urge people to think fully and deeply about what they ask for, and why and then detach from the outcome. Imagine that you have mailed a letter: Send the thought, then trust in its delivery. This technique is very powerful when an individual does not become obsessed or resentful about the outcome. It is also a way to help bring the body into alignment with the higher self because when we do this we enliven the mind-body connection. By asking for an end to our pain or illness, and by asking to understand its cause, we learn life's lessons and begin to understand our own truth.

This leads me to the topic of prayer. When most people pray they ask their higher power to **give** them something. I feel that prayer should also focus on asking for **removal** of whatever is stopping them from receiving what they are asking for. We should ask our higher power to dissolve any blockages or attitudes that hamper us from reaching our potential. When asking for healing I suggest that patients ask for the removal of anything - physical, emotional, chemical or spiritual - that is impeding their health. It may be something that they may have created or contributed to, such as issues with a mother or father, or maybe past hurts or resentments. It is not necessary to find the answers immediately, but more important to ask with intent. People can ask for guidance and clarity so that they can finally cancel any negative patterns and stop the damaging dance that they have been going through.

Many people are stuck in unhealthy relationships, which they blame on others. Instead of being victims they should place their attention on what they wish to clear away. One might ask to remove or heal the emotions that are causing the person to feel victimized. Then, just as after fasting we eat nourishing food, a person can start to focus on what they desire in a relationship and make that happen. I always ask: What do I need to learn from this? What did I do to create or allow this situation that is causing disharmony? When you **get** what you asked for, remember to thank the universe and yourself - because you are co-creators.

We exist on many levels. The most obvious is the physical, but keep in mind there are emotional and spiritual levels too. As we journey through life we encounter unique experiences and emotions. Some we wish to remember and savour, some we prefer to let go of. We want to remember those that embody lessons that can help us. Dreams, for example, may hold deep messages from our higher selves that we could benefit from even if we cannot completely understand them at the time.

At the same time many experiences are neither useful nor beneficial anymore, and some are actually holding us back through fear or anxiety. On a physical level our bodies work like computers collecting information and storing it. Just as a computer will crash if overloaded with information, so too will the body become lethargic and weighed down. Many experiences get "stuffed" inside because we need to get on with life, do our jobs, be effective parents, etc. This means there may not have been time to properly grieve when a friend died, or to think through a hurtful situation. The brain may not have time to process the experience all at once, so the body stores it away for future reference. Periodically, we should check our files, reflect upon them and then download those that are no longer beneficial, desirable or life supporting

The important concept here is: "Out with the old, in with the new." This does not mean avoiding the truth about ourselves and others, or deflecting issues without looking at them. The idea is to assist the body to cleanse itself of obstructions that may have become impediments to working through issues and stresses. I urge people to take advantage of Neural Organization or Neuro Emotional techniques, to read books on personal growth, see counselors or therapists, discuss feelings and opinions with others, and take time to be alone and in silence. This is how we begin to download and begin to understand others and ourselves. As we become clearer and lighter, our lives will begin to change on physical, emotional, and spiritual levels.

Below is a prayer of self-clearing that I have created for patients. They have all reported dramatic changes in their lives when they use it. Close your eyes, take a deep breath and when you feel centred and relaxed, begin to repeat the sentence below. Remember, it is not so much the specific wording that is important, but the intention that matters (i.e. out with the old, in with the new) and I have underlined the key elements to emphasize what we are trying to accomplish here:

"On all levels of my being, I wish to release the cause of all energies that I may harbour for any reason that are not serving the evolution of my higher self. I forgive myself and everyone for everything, now and forever."

You can go as far as your will will allow with this invocation, bearing in mind that the following four points are the key to co-creation with your higher power:

1. For clearing "on all levels of your being" you need to surrender your own personal concept of what may be causing your pain, condition or situation. This frees your higher mind to reach back to the source event.

2. This request can work on spiritual, emotional, physical and chemical levels to clear whatever needs to be released - **if you allow it.** For example, if you have a shoulder pain, is your intent to clear the pain on only a physical level, or are you willing to explore the emotion that may lie behind the pain? My advice is, do not limit your healing by a mistaken belief in the underlying cause.

3. Be willing to forgive all participants - including yourself. For example you may have an issue with trust. You may be holding onto old fear patterns based on a prior event where your mate was untrustworthy. Open your channel around issues of trust and relationships and once you have done that, ask to clear all its causes - forever. Next, visualize and let the body feel what it would be like to be in a relationship where you are completely trusting and trusted. Ask for what you really want, then **recognize** it when it has arrived, and walk through that open door.

4. Make the changes permanent. Your intention should be to clear this particular issue in the past, present and future, so you never have to deal with it again. Look honestly at the issues, release the negative, and **will** it to be permanent, i.e. now and forever.

This technique can be adapted to any situation. For example, if you are having trouble finding a trustworthy mate, your awareness has identified a source of disharmony in your life. To change it you merely follow the invocation, specifically asking to clear the cause of why you keep attracting untrustworthy partners.

If a pain is bothering you, try touching the point of pain, doing the invocation and asking to release its cause. Be patient, and be careful what you ask for because chances are you will receive it, and usually pretty quickly. When it does come there may be emotions involved that you never considered before. This is usually a blessing in disguise to help you heal and to move on, so never fear. Receive what comes with love, even it if does not feel great at the moment and keep in mind, it is the possibility of having a dream come true that makes life interesting.

Remember that you create all the situations in your life so instead of blaming the outside world and others for your unhappiness or dissatisfaction, take responsibility and will it to change. Most importantly do not try to change others for they are responsible for themselves. Rather, ask to clear the energies that you carry that are making you respond negatively to them. Undoing something means it is no longer a statement of who you want to be.

On the positive side, do not be ashamed to ask for things that you would like, such as a healthy body, happy loving friends, security for your family and a fulfilling job. Do not be afraid to ask the universe for anything. This is the power of co-creation. When you ask for something, also ask to be released from any thought pattern or belief system that is blocking you from receiving whatever you have just asked for. I frequently encourage people to ponder this saying: "We are spiritual beings having a human experience as well as human beings having a spiritual experience."

Over the years I have been able to not only sense human energy fields or "auras" but also to correct imbalances in them. How I do this is beyond the scope of this book, however, I assure you that there is nothing mystical about it. All of us are capable of changing our energy fields in a split second and assisting others to heal their energy fields too. Reiki, therapeutic touch, pranic healing, the laying on of hands, and a whole range of other techniques address the concept of healing through balancing the human energy field.

When I help to clear a patient's neuro-emotional "complex" I frequently find that their energy body changes as well, and these changes are often consistent and predictable for different emotional states. After making a correction to the physical or emotional body I can sense immediate changes in the energy body or aura. To verify what I am sensing, I can utilize muscle testing by holding my hand six to eight inches over the patient's body and seeing if there is a weak muscle response. Scientists use high tech equipment to authenticate the presence of human energy fields but I think that one day, through further scientific testing, it will be shown that muscle testing procedures can also be a tool used to verify the presence of human energy fields. This would involve further research. I have certainly met many people who can see auras, and who have verified these effects while watching me perform a treatment. Similarly I have many patients who have never known about the presence of human energy fields yet can immediately sense what I am doing, much to their amazement.

One patient in particular has a remarkable ability. She is a great lady and a wonderful mother who ensured that all her family came to see me before she sought treatment herself. She had no knowledge of auras or energetic bodywork, other than having been slightly introduced to my work by her family. Without any explanation of what I was going to do, I began treatment and in less than a minute, much to my surprise, she started smiling and saying, "Oh my God." I asked her what was happening and she reported seeing large waves of colour swirling around her body. As I moved my hands above specific areas of her body that I was treating, her eyes remained closed. She said: "Oh, it's blue around my legs, now it's green over my chest...." Then as I moved my hands to her head she immediately said: "Now my head is green. Oh, it's becoming purple on my face." I have seen her four or five times during the last three or four years and every time she has a similar sensory experience. She says she does not see auras at any other time, but is always amazed by the Aurora Borealis-like effect she experiences during treatments. It certainly adds credence to the saying that we are "light beings" and the fact that many people can actually see this reality.

It's time we awakened to our higher senses and became respectful of them, for if human energy fields exist then surely other energy fields may act upon them. We are constantly bombarded with invisible forces from computers, microwaves, cell phones, overhead transmission wires and much more, and these external influences may interfere with our own energies. We should look at their impact and consider them as a variable in health care today. Certainly this is becoming more and more evident as the Unified Field theory of modern physics now informs us that all matter - whether living or inanimate - is made up of particles vibrating at different frequencies.

Let it Flow

CHAPTER 7

PUTTING IT ALL TOGETHER

"Knowledge is a single point, but the foolish have multiplied it."

Sufi saying.

Now that I have explained the different techniques and approaches that I use, I can describe what actually happens during a session.

Using the N.O.T. protocols as my template for treatment means that I have a beginning and an end point to each of my sessions. I check the body in relation to the light, dark, eyes open and closed, sitting, standing, etc. and when a particular circuit shows weakness I ask the body if the cause is physical, emotional or chemical. The body will respond accordingly and I then use the appropriate technique to clear and recheck the involved circuit. This enables me to determine the root of the problem directly, without having to perform unnecessary corrections. It also employs the wisdom of the body to guide me, which increases accuracy.

For example, there is a program in the body that is labeled the "cranial reflex" in N.O.T. parlance. Its function is to hold or right the head on the body by stimulating the front and back muscles. If a person has had a blow to the head, this circuit can become disorganized and result in a condition that we call a "cranial injury complex." In 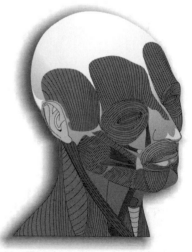 this instance the body loses its ability to hold the head up and goes into defence mode to protect itself against the possibility of another blow. Imagine a tent without four strong lines anchoring it to pegs in the ground: This is what the two sets of muscles at the front and back of the shoulders do when working correctly to support the head.

On a primitive level, the head must be held up so the body can defend itself, but in today's world survival is more complex. It may mean sitting all day in meetings or holding the head up so the eyes and brain can interact with a computer.

When a cranial injury complex exists, the body loses its ability to hold the head up properly. The animal cannot survive with its head drooping down at the ground as it needs to see what is in front of it, especially oncoming predators. Until this condition is properly corrected, the innate wisdom of the body tries to find a compensatory way to hold the head up. The brain orders more energy to the neck and shoulder muscles on the **back** of the body than the front. They become **hyper**tonic, while the front musculature that includes the chest muscles which assist in breathing and the abdominal muscles, become **hypo**tonic. As time passes, the back muscles end up doing most of the work and naturally start to fatigue and knot. This leads to tension across the neck and shoulders, making it difficult for the individual to stand erect with the shoulders back.

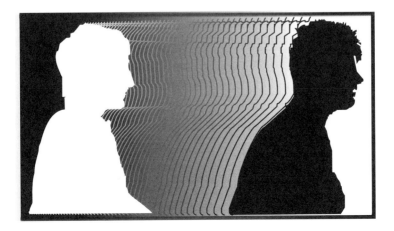

The base of the neck, which takes most of the strain, becomes increasingly rigid and inflexible as its muscles attempt to carry and brace the top-heavy skull. Often, if muscles alone fail to bolster the neck, the body starts laying down calcium in the unstable area, which eventually can be seen on X-ray imaging. This process of calcium buildup usually takes several years before becoming evident. The neck droops forward, a hump develops at its base, and the individual may eventually be diagnosed as having osteoarthritis. Few people look beyond this diagnosis for a reason why there is so-called arthritic degeneration of the neck, or why the body has chosen to adapt in this way. It is because the physiology is wisely responding in the best way it can to solidify an unstable area. A patient may be reconciled with the diagnosis when they hear they have arthritis of the neck because their mother had the same problem. Yet rather than blaming the condition on genetics it is far more accurate to deduce that the mother may have had similar cranial injuries in her childhood - as most of us do. We should not assume genetics is the culprit until we eliminate the other possibilities through muscle testing. It is important to understand that we should be testing body function, not merely following the trail of symptoms. If there is no cranial injury fault present we can then investigate further.

Overworked shoulder muscles and weak front muscles can result in poor abdominal strength (tummy muscles). The lower back, without the support of strong abdominal muscles, then becomes weakened due to that lack of support from this natural corset of muscles. The small and large intestines can start to sag inside the body, causing digestive complaints and diminished function. This has a domino effect on the lowest organs and systems in the body, namely the bladder, prostate gland (male) and uterus (female). The increased weight bearing down from above can lead to urine retention problems or painful periods for women, whereas in men, the prostate gland may become enlarged or swollen.

These symptoms may take 40 years to gradually manifest yet they all stem from a trauma to the head. Like a sweater with a loose thread, over time the loops start slowly unraveling until one day the garment is barely able to do its job. Should we wait until problems become severe, or should we see a Specialized Kinesiologist or someone specializing in N.O.T. for a systems check immediately after a trauma? Certainly the latter makes more sense. I have seen men and women with bladder and urinary ailments, as well as prolapsed organs, who sought surgical answers that failed to be effective. Yet they felt much better and experienced improvements in bowel and bladder function just days after N.O.T. treatments. Why? Once the neurological integrity is repaired the correct messages can get through to all sets of muscles and circuits - even after surgical intervention. Athletes report that they can do fewer sit-ups to achieve the same results and see dramatic improvements in exercise effectiveness.

My observations have led me to believe that the body stores emotional circuits together with physical circuits, and they correlate in the symbology of our language. For example the emotions of worry, lack of control, and poor self-esteem usually surface when correcting a cranial injury complex. We commonly acknowledge this relationship when we speak about people with emotional problems who are, "carrying the weight of the world on their shoulders," unable to "hold their head high," or needing to get something "off their chest." Sometimes I only have to correct the emotional component for the physical correction to occur, and vice-versa, although most often both the emotional and physical corrections need to be performed before the disorder disappears. By questioning the body I can determine which came first - the emotional or the physical trauma - but what is most important is that the cause be corrected and the condition not return.

Another example of these kinds of emotional-physical links involves the energy body. I commonly see women who have problems that relate to menstrual cycles: heavy or light flow, cramping, irregular frequency, and uterine cysts. Many women also have some form of low back pain, as well as irritation or weakness in the left neck or shoulder that is often misdiagnosed as carpal tunnel syndrome, bursitis and tendonitis. The real cause may stem from the reproductive/endocrine system, which has a neurologic connection to the left pectoralis major muscle, a prime stabilizer of the left shoulder. An imbalance in the female/male or reproductive circuits can result in a painful or restricted left arm, neck, or shoulder, which is why when anyone has these symptoms I always investigate the reproductive system.

What I will commonly find as the core cause of menstrual symptoms is the woman's subconscious rejection of her feminine energy or essence. This can occur for several emotional reasons, including sexual abuse, violation or rejection. One source of rejection that I commonly uncover occurs early in life when the female fetus or newborn senses that one of her parents is hoping for a male child. These feelings of being "unloved" or "unwanted" are stored in the uterus and ovary pathways of the female, and in the prostate and testicles in the male.

I recently treated a 35-year-old woman who, when asked to make the statement   "Females are wanted" or "Females are desirable," revealed through muscle testing that she did not believe this at a deep level - though consciously she thought she did. Further testing traced this condition all the way back to the first 'event' in the womb when she sensed that she was not unconditionally accepted. It didn't mean that her parents were hoping for a boy all the time that she was in the womb, nor does it suggest that her parents didn't accept and love her from the day she was born. The fact remains, her neurology blew "a tiny fuse" at that early moment when her mom or dad, or both, briefly pondered: "It would be neat if we have a boy." For some people's nervous system, this statement can become an "emotional reality" (i.e. they blow a "fuse") while in other cases the individual lets it go. Each person reacts differently and has different sensitivities, however, a weak circuit indicates it is an emotional reality for that body. I am not suggesting that parents should never think a negative thought about a child, nor am I proposing we become paranoid or guilty about how we feel and think. I am saying that we should clear the energy and set the record straight. We do this by stating our intent, as when saying the prayer in the previous chapter. Talk to your baby when he or she is in the womb and newly born and let it know of your total love. This may sound unbelievable to some, but I am convinced that we communicate on a much higher level than we give ourselves credit for.

The daughter who carries around this negative message may consciously think she is happy to be a woman, but subconsciously she may have some doubts. If her physical body is not 100 per cent congruent with her emotional body, then every time she tries to express her feminine self, as when she menstruates, there is subconscious resistance. Such incongruence can interfere with the function of various organs - in this case the uterus - which over time can show signs of disharmony, such as painful periods. It's as if the uterus is saying: "Pay attention. I'm wounded. I'm showing you something about yourself that is not harmonious." The same general idea applies to the male condition. When I see any dysfunction in "maleness" - a problem with the prostate gland or libido - I investigate the possibility of deep-seated imbalances relating to the masculine essence.

In all people there is a center located energetically over the pelvic region. It stores both our male and female power - which each one of us contains, to some degree. If there is an imbalance between the two aspects, the energy running up and down the person's core will be distorted or "off center." Another way of thinking about this is that the person cannot stand fully on his or her own two feet. There may be signs and symptoms of a repeatedly imbalanced sacrum and lumbar spine which traditional therapies have difficulty correcting. Not only would I correct the emotional cause in this instance, but I might also cleanse the energy field over the male-female center and perform a light correction to the sacrum or lumbar spine. This is a perfect example of physical, emotional, and spiritual or energetic healing all being done at once.

I may also encourage such patients to read books or have some emotional counseling, particularly about honouring the masculine-feminine aspects of their being, whichever is lacking. The patient may still need some chiropractic care to help stabilize the pelvic region, or some muscle therapy to loosen the muscles that have been subconsciously guarding that area for years.

Similar mind-to-body incongruence is also evident in people who have severe eating disorders. When anorexic young women look in the mirror they do not see their bodies as they actually are. They may be looking at a bony, dangerously thin reflection, but what they see is a hideously fat person carrying excess weight. I never need to ask these women if they love themselves - simply standing them in front of a mirror is enough to cause a significant drop in their energy, which can be verified by a weak muscle response. Even though they may have gone through extensive psychotherapy and consciously feel as if they can love and accept themselves, their bodies tell a different story. This incongruence between mind and body has made their recovery difficult and disheartening in the past, but that is changing now with techniques such as N.O.T. and N.E.T.® Interestingly, it might seem that this problem is limited to anorexia, since this disease relates to the acceptance of self, but my observations have revealed it is much more common than that. The truth is, **most** of us will show weak muscle responses when we look in a mirror and that is because the core issue behind many diseases is lack of self love.

Every person is like a new book to me - unique and fascinating because of his or her life experiences. However, common themes emerge from time to time and seem to be the threads that lead us to deeper understanding. They give me glimpses into the awesome connections between body, mind and spirit. Human beings are complex yet simple, like all great machines.

Let it Flow

CHAPTER 8

THE GLOBAL HEALTH MODEL

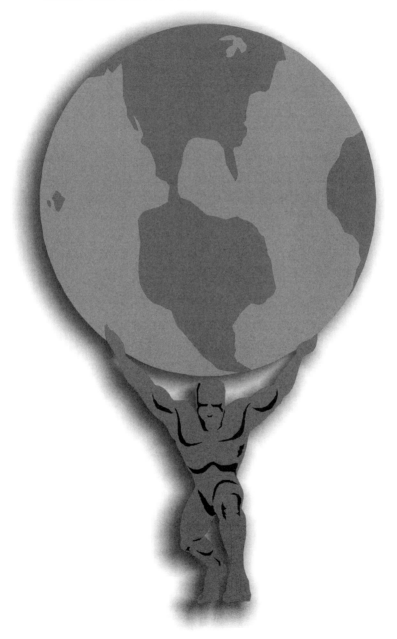

"A new Idea is first condemned as ridiculous and then dismissed as trivial, until finally, it becomes what everybody knows."

William James

The intent of this book is to present a model for health and wellness that is effective for every person and every discipline. That sounds like a tall order, but I think it is completely possible if a health practitioner bases his treatments and techniques on the true fundamentals of health.

While doing research recently in the health and wellness section of a major bookstore I was pleased to see how many books have been written about the role that emotional well being plays in everyone's life. There are books on modifying the way one eats, thinks, sleeps, prays and perceives life. There are books on exercises, yoga, Qi Gong, Tai Chi, stretching and athletics. Equally important are the books on chakras, the spiritual body, the soul, past lives, and higher metaphysical or spiritual teachings.

All these books assist people to help themselves, but I wonder how a person can effectively exercise or achieve optimal performance if their nervous system is disorganized and keeping them out of balance? How can a person modify their diet to achieve a desired state of health when the nervous system that controls their digestive function is in disarray? How can one successfully perform affirmations and move forward emotionally and spiritually if their nervous system is still locked into past events that inhibit the flow of life? Similarly, how can one effectively clear an imbalance of the aura and its chakras if the physical body is stuck in neural disorganization?

The physical hands-on reorganization of a person's nervous system is the essential variable that needs to be seriously addressed before any truly consistent and authentic research claims can be made.

The techniques and theories presented in this book are all related to one another on some level. My hope is to one day see a health care system that is based on a model that integrates these different systems in a logical and systematic way, guided by the wisdom of the body.

For example, if a patient breaks a leg, the first thing that needs to be done is setting and casting the leg. But it is important to work backwards in our thinking if we are to treat the whole person. The nervous system has several "safety switches" which alert the brain whenever the skin, muscles and finally the bone are in danger of being ripped or broken. If one stretches a muscle beyond its normal range the brain immediately shuts off the nerve supply to prevent serious damage to that muscle. If you have ever lifted something too heavy you know what I mean. Something inside of you makes you stop lifting the object or even tells you to drop it. These circuits will almost always be "in fault" after a bone is broken because in order for the break to occur the traumatic force had to be so strong and so fast that it would blow all the safety breakers first, in a matter of milliseconds.

Bearing this in mind, the next logical step to ensure a speedy and efficient recovery, after setting and casting the broken bone, would be to perform the N.O.T. procedures. This reactivates and returns function to the primitive reflexes that keep the head, shoulders, pelvis, hips, knees and ankles level with the ground. The next step would be to perform soft tissue rehabilitation and massage to break up the scar tissue. A few Chiropractic adjustments might be needed to realign the structure and mobilize the joints, followed by instruction in exercises to carry on at home, to strengthen the muscles. Such exercises might even **improve** previous muscle tone and, since poor tone may have been why the person broke a bone in the first place, this is an essential part of rehabilitation.

If the nervous system reflexes are **not** corrected after a serious fall or injury then the following scenario is typical: First, the body must compensate for any imbalance or misalignment. This usually means that the pelvis, knee, ankle and foot on one side of the body start to take excessive stresses. Second, tissue repair is hampered because the body is in a hurry to get back to balance. Lower quality tissue (i.e. scar tissue) is built up because the body responds this way in an emergency. (If the body were immediately rebalanced and therefore not under undue stress, it would heal gradually and correctly.) Excessive scar tissue buildup can cause problems down the road. Being non-elastic tissue, it can restrict range of motion, flexibility and cause stiffness, pain and perhaps lead to further accidents and degenerative conditions.

The problem of excess scar tissue layers can sometimes be repaired later, but it calls for many sessions of sometimes painful soft tissue therapies, trigger point therapies and time consuming hands-on work to break up the tissues. All this can be avoided by doing the correct balancing work immediately after the accident, followed by effective rehabilitation to ensure that scar tissue is minimized and primary elastic tissue is recreated instead.

I have seen many patients who have gone through this scenario. They have had an accident or broken a bone that healed, but other problems started to arise within a short period of time. They were put through countless sessions of physiotherapy, which never completely restored the range of motion because their pelvis and lower back were still misaligned. They saw chiropractors, massage therapists and many other mainstream and complementary health practitioners, all to no avail. No matter how many adjustments were performed, as soon as they got off the therapist's table and stood up again the pelvis began to go out of alignment. They may not have felt the symptoms return immediately, but within a short time they felt their pelvis was "out again". Why? Because the nervous system reflexes were still disorganized and turned off causing the body to react that way! These patients are typically given endless doses of painkillers or anti-inflammatories which just mask the problem. Worse yet, the pills significantly irritate the digestive system and produce other problems in the body. They do not get significantly better as time goes by, and find that they no longer have the same use of their leg and body - even though the broken bone has healed. This may eventually interfere with their abilities to work and they may have to change jobs, which places stress on the whole family and may lead to the patient feeling depressed and emotionally fatigued. So it's back to the medical doctor for some anti-depressants, and the story goes on.

Obviously the above scenario does not occur in every case of a broken leg, but I have worked on enough people around the world to know it is all too common. It doesn't have to be a broken bone or structural concern for this kind of scenario to start to play in a person's life. If a patient has dyslexia, hormonal imbalances or even digestive problems these kinds of events can begin to affect someone's life on all levels. First by interfering with their function, then their families, their jobs, their self-esteem and eventually their mental state.

We all pay the cost.

Not only does it significantly affect a person's life, but also those around him or her. It causes unnecessary suffering.

It costs the system incredible amounts of money because we have accepted many conditions as "chronic" and irreparable when they can clearly be fixed. Once a condition is labeled chronic it seems suddenly to justify many more treatments to correct or manage it. I challenge this mode of thinking because I have seen so-called chronic conditions change in minutes or hours using the methods described in this book. Health care providers are either lazy or ignorant if they claim that their modality is the only solution to the problem. What's worse is when they state that if they cannot fix it then nothing can, and then tell their patients to learn to live with it. This is not only arrogant but a very defeatist attitude. What I prefer to tell patients is that every day we are accumulating more and more knowledge and insights, and when health professionals and complementary practitioners work together we can solve many of the problems that are plaguing our society.

We must continue asking questions so that we can unravel the mysteries of the body and its relation to the universe we live in. We must stop ignoring the answers that lie within the human body itself, along with the means to correct these problems.

Much credit should be given to the pioneers of Chiropractic and Applied Kinesiology who had the wisdom and humility to let the body be the Master Doctor. They used their knowledge of the nervous system and its relationship to physiology to unlock the potent and profound techniques described in this book. The power that made the body is the power that heals the body - we should listen to it and trust in its infinite intelligence to guide us.

I appeal to all health care providers and agencies, to governments, insurance companies, and all wellness centers and hospitals to open their minds and research dollars to investigating these innovative and effective techniques. The work described in this book requires no more than one to four treatment sessions, and once the corrections are made they are **lasting** - i.e. neurological integrity will hold - unless there is a new trauma. It is powerful, repeatable, and reproducible on everyone and its cost effectiveness surpasses anything I have yet to study or read about. These are primitive, innate circuits and reflexes that exist in all people and animals. The emotional state, spiritual well being, diet, exercise and so on will always be variables in any wellness profile, but 10 years of clinical experience in treating more than 8,000 people globally has shown me the effectiveness of this program.

This work must be given a chance to prove itself and to show its efficacy. The present day system is out of control and must be changed. I am available to present lectures and do research projects, as well as to consult with governments, groups and agencies so that we can restructure our present day health care system. The future is ours to create.

Namaste.

For further information and contact:
www.drsheeltangri.com

Let it Flow

REFERENCES, BIBLIOGRAPHY and RECOMMENDED READING

Leach, Robert A. The Chiropractic Theories 2nd ed. Baltimore, MD.: Williams and Wilkins. 1986.

Kapit, Wynn and Robert I. Macey and Esmail Meisami. The Physiology Coloring Book. New York N. Y.: Harper and Row, 1987.

Kapit, Wynn and Lawrence M. Elson. The Anatomy Coloring Book. New York, N.Y.: Harper and Row, 1977.

Walther, David S. Applied Kinesiology: Synopsis. Pueblo Colorado: Systems D.C., 1988.

Thie, John F. Touch for Health. Pasadena, California: T. H. Enterprises, 1987.

Promislow, Sharon. Making the Brain/Body Connection, 2nd ed. West Vancouver. B.C. Kinetic Publishing Corporation, 1998.

Upledger, J. E., and Uredevoogd, J. D., Craniosacral Therapy. Seattle, WA: Eastland Press, 1983.

Pansky, Ben. Review of Gross Anatomy, 5th ed. New York, N.Y.: Macmillan Publishing Company, 1984.

Bogduk, Nikolai and Twomey, Lance T. Clinical Anatomy of the Lumbar Spine. New York, N. Y.: Churchill Livingstone, 1987.

Pert, Candace B. Molecules of Emotion.. New York, N. Y.: Scribner, 1997.

Diamond, Harvey and Marilyn. Fit for Life. New York, N. Y.: Warner Books, 1985.

Matsen, John. Eating Alive: Prevention Through Good Digestion. North Vancouver, B.C.: Crompton Books, Ltd., 1987.

Guyton, Arthur C. Textbook of Medical Physiology. Philadelphia, PA.: W. B. Saunders Company, 1986.

Chopra, Deepak. Quantum Healing: Exploring the Frontiers of Mind/Body Medicine. New York, N. Y.: Bantam Books, 1989.

* Brennan, Barbara Ann. Light Emerging: The Journey of Personal Healing. New York , N. Y.: Bantam Books, 1993.

Brennan, Barbara Ann. Hands of Light: A guide to Healing Through the Human Energy Field. New York, N. Y.: Bantam Books, 1987.

* Hay, Louise L. You Can Heal Your Life. Santa Monica, CA.: Hay House, 1982.

* Hay, Louise L. Heal Your Body. Carson, CA.: Hay House, 1988.

Govan, A.D.T, Macfarlane, P.S., and Callander, R. Pathology Illustrated, 2nd edition. United Kingdom: Churchill Livingstone, 1986.

Ferreri, Carl A. N.O.T. Technique Manual of Basic Philosophy and Concepts.

Beinfield, Harriet and Korngold, Efrem. Between Heaven and Earth: A Guide to Chinese Medicine. New York: Ballantine Books, 1991.

Callahan, R. and Callahan, J. Thought Field Therapy and Training: treatment and theory. Thought Field Training Centre, Indian Wells. CA. 92210. 1996
Craig. G. and Fowlie, A. Emotional Freedom Techniques. Cary Craig, P.O. Box 398, The Sea Ranch, CA. 95497. 1995.

Gallo, Fred. Energy Psychology. CRC Press, Bocca Raton, FL. 1998.

Burrows, Stanley. The Master Cleanser. Reno, NV: Burroughts Books, 1976.

* Chopra, Deepak. The Seven Spiritual Laws of Success. Amber-Allen Publishing, (some date missing here, need city and state) 1994.

* Myss, Caroline. Anatomy of the Spirit.. New York, N.Y.: Crown Publishers. Inc., 1996.

* Newton, Michael. Journey of Souls. 5th ed.. St. Paul, MN.: Llewellyn Publications, 1994.

* Tolle, Eckhart. The Power of Now. Vancouver, B.C.: Namaste Publishing, 1997.

Peterson, Kristopher B., Two cases of spinal manipulation performed while the patient contemplated an associated stress event: the effect of the manipulation/contemplation on serum cholesterol levels in hypercholesterolemic subjects. Chiropractic Technique, 1995; 7(2); 55-59.

Peterson, Kristopher, B. , A Preliminary Inquiry into Manual Muscle Testing Response in Phobic and Control Subjects Exposed to Threatening Stimuli, JMPT, 1996; 19(5): 310-316.

D' Adamo, Peter J. Eat Right For Your Type. New York, N.Y.: G.P. Putnams Sons,1996.